Going Places

A Person is a Person

Approaches to Visible Voices

Credits and acknowledgements

Visible Voices has been produced in association with the **Anthology** unit from the Channel 4 Schools series **The English Programme**.

Anthology is produced for Channel 4 Schools by **Double Exposure**. Produced by **Peter Griffiths** and **Rachel Thomas**.

Visible Voices is edited by **Michael Jones** and illustrated by **Melvyn Evans**. Cover illustration by **Melvyn Evans**.

First published 1994 by
The Educational Television
Company Limited
10a Great Titchfield Street
London W1P 7AA

British Library Cataloguing in Publication Data.

A catalogue record for this book is available from the British Library.

ISBN 1 899214 05 4

This edition © The Educational Television Company Limited 1994.

Designed by **Jean Miller Design**.
Typeset by **Balance Type**.
All rights reserved.

We acknowledge the copyright of the following and thank them for permission to reproduce their poems:
John Agard c/o Caroline Sheldon Literary Agency for his poems 'Palm Tree King' and 'Stereotype' from *Mangoes & Bullets*, published by Pluto Press, 1985; and 'First black man in space' from *Angels of Fire*, first published 1986. **Anvil Press Poetry Ltd.** for 'Misunderstanding and Muzak' from *Long Story Short* by Dennis O'Driscoll, 1993. **James Bernard** for 'Gutter Press' by Paul Dehn. **Bloodaxe Books Ltd.** for 'It Ain't What You Do It's What It Does To You' from *Zoom* by Simon Armitage, 1989. **Valerie Bloom** for her poems 'Wha Fe Call I' and 'Yuh Hear Bout?' from *Touch Mi, Tell Mi*, published by Bogle L'Ouverture Publications, 1983 (reprinted 1990). **Carcanet Press Ltd.** for 'Buffaloes' from *Brunizem* by Sujata Bhatt; 'Sunday', 'My Box', and 'Suicide on Pentwyn Bridge' from *Selected Poems* by Gillian Clarke; 'Neighbours' from *Letting in the Rumour* by Gillian Clarke; and 'In the Children's Hospital' from *Selected Poems* by Hugh MacDiarmid. **Gillian Clarke** for her poem 'The Field-Mouse'. **John Cooper Clarke** for his poems 'R U the Business?' and 'i wanna be yours'. **Faber and Faber Ltd.** for 'The Plantation' from *Door into the Dark* by Seamus Heaney; 'Mid-Term Break' from *Death of a Naturalist* by Seamus Heaney; 'From the Frontier of Writing' and 'From the Republic of Conscience' from *The Haw Lantern* by Seamus Heaney; 'The Unknown Citizen' from *Collected Shorter Poems 1927 –1957* by W. H. Auden; 'Song' from *Collected Poems* by W. H. Auden, ed.

Edward Mendelson; Morning Song' from *Ariel* by Sylvia Plath; 'Born Yesterday' from *Collected Poems* by Philip Larkin; 'The Metaphor Now Standing At Platform 8' from *Kid* by Simon Armitage; and 'Midsummer, Tobago' from *Collected Poems 1948 –1984* by Derek Walcott. **Nilene O A Foxworth** for her poem 'SHO NUFF'. **The Gallery Press** for 'Claudy' from *Poems 1956 –1986* by James Simmons. **Tony Harrison** for his poems 'Long Distance II', 'Book Ends' and 'Timer'. **David Higham Associates** for 'Life Is Fine' from *Selected Poems* by Langston Hughes, published by Vintage; 'Mirrors' from *Collected Poems* by Elizabeth Jennings, published by Carcanet Press Ltd.; 'Do Not Go Gentle into That Good Night' and 'The Hand that Signed the Paper' from *The Poems* by Dylan Thomas, published by J. M. Dent; and 'Remember?' from *Horses Make a Landscape Look More Beautiful* by Alice Walker, published by The Women's Press Ltd., 1985. **John Johnson Ltd.** for 'Warning' from *Selected Poems* by Jenny Joseph, published by Bloodaxe Books Ltd., © Jenny Joseph, 1992. **Karnak House** for 'Like a Flame', an extract from 'I Go To Meet Him' from *i is a long memoried woman* by Grace Nichols, © Karnak House 1983, 1990. **Tom Leonard** for his poem 'A Summer's Day' from *Intimate Voices*, published by Vintage. **Vasa D. Mihailovich** for his translation of 'For Lies Spoken out of Kindness' by Desanka Maksimović. **W.W. Norton & Company Ltd.** for 'somewhere i have never travelled, gladly beyond' from *Complete Poems 1904 –1962* by E.E. Cummings, edited by George J. Firmage, copyright © 1931, 1979, 1991 by the Trustees for the E.E. Cummings Trust and George James Firmage. **Oxford University Press** for 'Behaviour of Fish in an Egyptian Tea Garden' from *The Complete Poems of Keith Douglas*, ed. Desmond Graham, 1978, © Marie J. Douglas, 1978; 'Naming of Parts' by Henry Reed from *Collected Poems*, ed. Jon Stallworthy, 1991; and 'A Martian Sends a Postcard Home' from *A Martian Sends a Postcard Home* by Craig Raine, 1979. **Penguin Books Ltd.** for 'Class Game' by Mary Casey from *I Wouldn't Thank You for a Valentine* by Carol Ann Duffy, © Mary Casey, 1992; and 'When You're a GROWN-UP...' by Michael Rosen from *You Tell Me*, copyright © Michael Rosen, 1979, first published by Viking Children's Books. **Peterloo Poets** for 'Not My Best Side' by U. A. Fanthorpe from *Side Effects*, 1978, © U. A. Fanthorpe; 'Growing Up' by U. A. Fanthorpe from *Voices Off*, 1984, © U. A. Fanthorpe; and 'First Flight' by U. A. Fanthorpe from *A Watching Reef*, 1987, © U. A. Fanthorpe. **Peters, Fraser and Dunlop Group Ltd.** for 'The Skip' from *The Memory of War* by James Fenton; and 'Saw It In The Papers' by Adrian Mitchell, from *Adrian Mitchell's Greatest Hits – The Top 40*, published by Bloodaxe Books Ltd. (None of Adrian Mitchell's poems are to be used in connection with any examination whatsoever). **Polygon** for 'What-I'm-Not Song' and 'I Wouldn't Thank You for a Valentine' from *True Confessions* by Liz Lochhead; and 'The Choosing' and 'The Visit' from *Dreaming Frankenstein* by Liz Lochhead. **Simon Rae** for 'Lessons of the War' from *Klaonica Poems for Bosnia*, published by Bloodaxe Books Ltd., originally published in *The Guardian*. **Kathleen Raine** for her poem 'Amo Ergo Sum'. **Random House UK Ltd.** for 'Out, Out –' by Robert Frost from *The Poetry of Robert Frost*, ed. Edward Connery Lathem. **Annette Robertson** for her poem 'I Tell You I Don't Love You'. **Rogers, Coleridge & White Ltd.** for 'A Poem For A Very Special Person' from *My Granny is a Sumo Wrestler* by Gareth Owen, published by Young Lions, 1994, © Gareth Owen 1994. **Kim R Stafford** for 'Travelling Through the Dark' by William Stafford. **Trentham Books Ltd.** for 'September Assignment' by Mike Kivi from *Verse to Reverse the Classroom Blues*, 1993. **Virago Press Ltd.** for 'Even Tho' from *Lazy Thoughts of a Lazy Woman and Other Poems* by Grace Nichols, 1989; and 'The Fat Black Woman's Instructions to a Suitor' from *The Fat Black Woman's Poems* by Grace Nichols, 1984. **Raymond Wilson** for his poem 'This Letter's to Say'. **Jim Wong-Chu** for his poem 'equal opportunity'. **Benjamin Zephaniah** for his poem 'No Problem'.
The Publishers have made every attempt to trace the copyright holders, but in cases where they have failed will be pleased to make the necessary arrangements at the first opportunity.

Introduction

> 'Finding a voice means that you can get your own feeling into your own words and that your words have the feel of you about them.'
>
> **SEAMUS HEANEY**

Visible Voices is a poetry anthology linked with the Channel 4 Schools series **The English Programme.** The book, like the programmes, offers poetry that reflects the pressures and the pleasures of human experience through poems that are challenging as well as enjoyable. It contains a deliberate variety of voices – ancient and modern, black and white, male and female. The poems are grouped into sections with the same thematic focus as the programmes, and the order in which poems appear in the programmes is usually preserved in the book to make it easier to link looking, listening and reading.

This is a collection for anyone who reads poetry, but it is also ideal as a basis for study at GCSE level, Standard Grade (Scotland) and beyond. The range of poems included covers all the requirements of the National Curriculum for English, and there are suggestions about ways of studying the poems. There are various starting points for study through themes, authors and styles, and there is an individual poet featured in each section. Each of these poets, Tony Harrison, Gillian Clarke, Grace Nichols, Seamus Heaney and Liz Lochhead, is represented by at least three poems.

Each section contains pre-20th-century poems alongside poems by emerging contemporary authors and well-established ones. The range of cultures represented is wide, and although there is an unashamedly high profile for some of the best-known poems in English literature, this is complemented by other voices. Many styles and forms of poetry are included. The placing of the poems is often intended to encourage contrast or comparison, and the illustrations which accompany the poems have voices of their own.

MICHAEL JONES was a teacher for eleven years and Head of English in two comprehensive schools. He is now English Adviser for Cheshire and was Chair of the National Association for Advisers in English. Currently Chair of Examiners for NEAB, he is also an accredited OFSTED inspector. His hobbies include attending NATE conferences, writing articles in defence of English teachers and editing materials for schools.

A Matter of Life and Death

Poetry is a matter of life and death, not because it makes things happen in the outer world, but because it can influence our inner worlds. Poetry is very much a matter of learning about living and dying. It helps us to see who we are and to know how we feel. Poems are a way of exploring and sharing experience by putting language under the pressure of feeling and form.

The poems in this section begin at the beginning with poems about birth by Sylvia Plath and Philip Larkin, and they end with the poem that Dylan Thomas wrote to his dying father. In between there is suffering in Robert Frost's 'Out, Out –' and sorrow in 'Mid-Term Break' by Seamus Heaney, but also joy in the poem by the ancient Persian writer Mahsati and, despite the loss of his love, in the poem by Langston Hughes. The death of a deer prompts William Stafford into thinking hard about the ways in which, in some senses, we are all just travellers in the dark. Life is celebrated by Walt Whitman and thrown into a skip by James Fenton.

There is a sequence of poems in which poets reflect on death and dying. These include Wordsworth's short but intensely powerful 'A slumber did my spirit seal', Christina Rossetti's sonnet about how she would want to be remembered and Gillian Clarke's poem about a suicide. Amongst the most moving of these are the poems written by Tony Harrison after the death of his mother.

The two final poems, written centuries apart, have complex but conventional rhyme schemes. They are John Donne's sonnet 'Death Be Not Proud' and 'Do Not Go Gentle into That Good Night' by Dylan Thomas, which is in the form of a villanelle. These poems are reminders that as readers we respond to form and content together. Seamus Heaney gave an author's-eye view when writing about what a poet tries to do through technique:

'Technique entails the watermarking of your essential patterns of perception, voice and thought into the touch and texture of your lines; it is that whole creative effort of the mind's and body's resources to bring the meaning of experience within the jurisdiction of form. Technique is what turns, in Yeats's phrase, "the bundle of accident and incoherence that sits down to breakfast" into "an idea, something intended, complete."'

Life, unlike poetry, is rarely intended or complete, but poems can help us to endure and to enjoy it.

Morning Song

Love set you going like a fat gold watch.
The midwife slapped your footsoles, and your bald cry
Took its place among the elements.

Our voices echo, magnifying your arrival. New statue.
In a drafty museum, your nakedness
Shadows our safety. We stand round blankly as walls.

I'm no more your mother
Than the cloud that distils a mirror to reflect its own slow
Effacement at the wind's hand.

All night your moth-breath
Flickers among the flat pink roses. I wake to listen:
A far sea moves in my ear.

One cry, and I stumble from bed, cow-heavy and floral
In my Victorian nightgown.
Your mouth opens clean as a cat's. The window square

Whitens and swallows its dull stars. And now you try
Your handful of notes;
The clear vowels rise like balloons.

7

Born Yesterday

for Sally Amis

Tightly-folded bud,
I have wished you something
None of the others would:
Not the usual stuff
About being beautiful,
Or running off a spring
Of innocence and love –
They will all wish you that,
And should it prove possible,
Well, you're a lucky girl.

But if it shouldn't, then
May you be ordinary;
Have, like other women,
An average of talents:
Not ugly, not good-looking,
Nothing uncustomary
To pull you off your balance,
That, unworkable itself,
Stops all the rest from working.
In fact, may you be dull –
If that is what a skilled,
Vigilant, flexible,
Unemphasised, enthralled
Catching of happiness is called.

'Out, Out –'

The buzz saw snarled and rattled in the yard
And made dust and dropped stove-length sticks of wood,
Sweet-scented stuff when the breeze drew across it.
And from there those that lifted eyes could count
Five mountain ranges one behind the other
Under the sunset far into Vermont.
And the saw snarled and rattled, snarled and rattled,
As it ran light, or had to bear a load.
And nothing happened: day was all but done.
Call it a day, I wish they might have said
To please the boy by giving him the half hour
That a boy counts so much when saved from work.
His sister stood beside them in her apron
To tell them 'Supper'. At the word, the saw,
As if to prove saws knew what supper meant,
Leaped out at the boy's hand, or seemed to leap –
He must have given the hand. However it was,
Neither refused the meeting. But the hand!
The boy's first outcry was a rueful laugh,
As he swung toward them holding up the hand,
Half in appeal, but half as if to keep
The life from spilling. Then the boy saw all –
Since he was old enough to know, big boy
Doing a man's work, though a child at heart –
He saw all spoiled. 'Don't let him cut my hand off –
The doctor, when he comes. Don't let him, sister!'
So. But the hand was gone already.
The doctor put him in the dark of ether.
He lay and puffed his lips out with his breath.
And then – the watcher at his pulse took fright.
No one believed. They listened at his heart.
Little – less – nothing! – and that ended it.
No more to build on there. And they, since they
Were not the one dead, turned to their affairs.

9

Mid-Term

I sat all morning in the college sick bay
Counting bells knelling classes to a close.
At two o'clock our neighbours drove me home.

In the porch I met my father crying –
He had always taken funerals in his stride –
And Big Jim Evans saying it was a hard blow.

The baby cooed and laughed and rocked the pram
When I came in, and I was embarrassed
By old men standing up to shake my hand

And tell me they were 'sorry for my trouble',
Whispers informed strangers I was the eldest,
Away at school, as my mother held my hand

In hers and coughed out angry tearless sighs.
At ten o'clock the ambulance arrived
With the corpse, stanched and bandaged by the nurses.

Next morning I went up into the room. Snowdrops
And candles soothed the bedside; I saw him
For the first time in six weeks. Paler now,

Wearing a poppy bruise on his left temple,
He lay in the four foot box as in his cot.
No gaudy scars, the bumper knocked him clear.

A four foot box, a foot for every year.

Break

Quatrains

Better to live as a rogue and a bum,
     a lover all treat as a joke,
to hang out with a crowd of comfortable drunks,
     than crouch in a hypocrite's cloak.

Unless you can dance through a common bar
     with a vagabond's step, you're not going to make it.
This is the road of the reckless who gamble
     their lives; risk yours, or you're not going to make it.

(translated from Farsi by Deirdre Lashgari)

11

Life Is Fine

I went down to the river,
I set down on the bank.
I tried to think but couldn't,
So I jumped in and sank.

I came up once and hollered!
I came up twice and cried!
If that water hadn't a-been so cold
I might've sunk and died.

But it was
Cold in that water!
It was cold!

I took the elevator
Sixteen floors above the ground.
I thought about my baby
And thought I would jump down.

I stood there and I hollered!
I stood there and I cried!
If it hadn't a-been so high
I might've jumped and died.

But it was
High up there!
It was high!

So since I'm still here livin',
I guess I will live on.
I could've died for love –
But for livin' I was born.

Though you may hear me holler,
And you may see me cry –
I'll be dogged, sweet baby,
If you gonna see me die.

Life is fine!
Fine as wine!
Life is fine!

Travelling Through the

Dark

Travelling through the dark I found a deer
dead on the edge of the Wilson River road.
It is usually best to roll them into the canyon:
that road is narrow; to swerve might make more dead.

By glow of the tail-light I stumbled back of the car
and stood by the heap, a doe, a recent killing;
she had stiffened already, almost cold.
I dragged her off; she was large in the belly.

My fingers touching her side brought me the reason –
her side was warm; her fawn lay there waiting,
alive, still, never to be born.
Beside that mountain road I hesitated.

The car aimed ahead its lowered parking lights;
under the hood purred the steady engine.
I stood in the glare of the warm exhaust turning red;
around our group I could hear the wilderness listen.

I thought hard for us all – my only swerving –
then pushed her over the edge into the river.

13

Give Me

the Splendid Silent Sun

Give me the splendid silent sun with all his beams full-
    dazzling,
Give me juicy autumnal fruit ripe and red from the
    orchard,
Give me a field where the unmowed grass grows,
Give me an arbour, give me the trellised grape,
Give me fresh corn and wheat, give me serene-moving
    animals teaching content,
Give me nights perfectly quiet as on high plateaus west of
    the Mississippi, and I looking up at the stars,

Give me odorous at sunrise a garden of beautiful flowers
    where I can walk undisturbed,
Give me for marriage a sweet-breathed woman of whom I
    should never tire,
Give me a perfect child, give me away aside from the noise
    of the world a rural domestic life,
Give me to warble spontaneous songs recluse by myself, for
    my own ears only,
Give me solitude, give me Nature, give me again, O Nature,
    your primal sanities!

T^{he} S^ki^p

JAMES FENTON

I took my life and threw it on the skip,
Reckoning the next-door neighbours wouldn't mind
If my life hitched a lift to the council tip
With their dry rot and rubble. What you find

With skips is – the whole community joins in.
Old mattresses appear, doors kind of drift
Along with all that won't fit in the bin
And what the bin-men can't be fished to shift.

I threw away my life, and there it lay
And grew quite sodden. 'What a dreadful shame,'
Clucked some old bag and sucked her teeth: 'The way
The young these days... no values... me, I blame...'

But I blamed no one. Quality control
Had loused it up, and that was that. 'Nough said.
I couldn't stick at home. I took a stroll
And passed the skip, and left my life for dead.

Without my life, the beer was just as foul,
The landlord still as filthy as his wife,
The chicken in the basket was an owl,
And no one said: 'Ee, Jim-lad, whur's thee life?'

Well, I got back that night the worse for wear,
But still just capable of single vision;
Looked in the skip; my life – it wasn't there!
Some bugger'd nicked it – *without* my permission.

Okay, so I got angry and began
To shout, and woke the street. Okay. *Okay!*
And I was sick all down the neighbour's van.
And I disgraced myself on the par-*kay*.

And then... you know how if you've had a few
You'll wake at dawn, all healthy, like sea breezes,
Raring to go, and thinking: 'Clever you!
You've got away with it.' And then, oh Jesus,

It hits you. Well, that morning, just at six
I woke, got up and looked down at the skip.
There lay my life, still sodden, on the bricks;
There lay my poor old life, arse over tip.

Or was it mine? Still dressed, I went downstairs
And took a long cool look. The truth was dawning.
Someone had just exchanged my life for theirs.
Poor fool, I thought – I should have left a warning.

Some bastard saw my life and thought it nicer
Than what he had. Yet what he'd had seemed fine.
He'd never caught his fingers in the slicer
The way I'd managed in that life of mine.

His life lay glistening in the rain, neglected,
Yet still a decent, an authentic life.
Some people I can think of, I reflected
Would take that thing as soon as you'd say Knife.

It seemed a shame to miss a chance like that.
I brought the life in, dried it by the stove.
It looked so fetching, stretched out on the mat.
I tried it on. It fitted, like a glove.

And now, when some local bat drops off the twig
And new folk take the house, and pull up floors
And knock down walls and hire some kind of big
Container (say, a skip) for their old doors,

I'll watch it like a hawk, and every day
I'll make at least – oh – half a dozen trips.
I've furnished an existence in that way.
You'd not believe the things you find on skips.

17

A slumber did my spirit seal;
   I had no human fears:
She seemed a thing that could not feel
   The touch of earthly years.

No motion has she now, no force;
   She neither hears nor sees;
Rolled round in earth's diurnal course,
   With rocks, and stones, and trees.

Remember

Remember me when I am gone away,
     Gone far away into the silent land;
     When you can no more hold me by the hand,
Nor I half turn to go, yet turning stay.
Remember me when no more day by day
     You tell me of our future that you plann'd:
     Only remember me; you understand
It will be late to counsel then or pray.
Yet if you should forget me for a while
     And afterwards remember, do not grieve:
     For if the darkness and corruption leave
     A vestige of the thoughts that I once had,
Better by far you should forget and smile
     Than that you should remember and be sad.

Suicide on Pentwyn Bridge

I didn't know him,
the man who jumped from the bridge.
But I saw the parabola
of long-drawn-out falling in the brown

eyes of his wife week after week
at the supermarket cash-out.
We would quietly ask "How is he?"
hear of the hospital's white

care, the corridors between her
and the broken man in the bed,
and the doctors who had no words,
no common supermarket women's talk.

Only after the funeral
I knew how he'd risen, wild
from his chair and told her
he was going out to die.

Very slowly from the first leap
he fell through winter, through the cold
of Christmas, wifely silences,
the blue scare of ambulance,

from his grave on the motorway
to the hospital, two bridges down.
A season later in a slow cortège
he has reached the ground.

Long Distance II

Though my mother was already two years dead
Dad kept her slippers warming by the gas,
put hot water bottles her side of the bed
and still went to renew her transport pass.

You couldn't just drop in. You had to phone.
He'd put you off an hour to give him time
to clear away her things and look alone
as though his still raw love were such a crime.

He couldn't risk my blight of disbelief
though sure that very soon he'd hear her key
scrape in the rusted lock and end his grief.
He *knew* she'd just popped out to get the tea.

I believe life ends with death, and that is all.
You haven't both gone shopping; just the same,
in my new black leather phone book there's your name
and the disconnected number I still call.

21

Book Ends

Baked the day she suddenly dropped dead
we chew it slowly that last apple pie.

Shocked into sleeplessness you're scared of bed.
We never could talk much, and now don't try.

You're like book ends, the pair of you, she'd say,
Hog that grate, say nothing, sit, sleep, stare ...

The 'scholar' me, you, worn out on poor pay,
only our silence made us seem a pair.

Not as good for staring in, blue gas,
too regular each bud, each yellow spike.

A night you need my company to pass
and she not here to tell us we're alike!

Your life's all shattered into smithereens.

Back in our silences and sullen looks,
for all the Scotch we drink, what's still between 's
not the thirty or so years, but books, books, books.

Timer

Gold survives the fire that's hot enough
to make you ashes in a standard urn.
An envelope of coarse official buff
contains your wedding ring which wouldn't burn.

Dad told me I'd to tell them at St James's
that the ring should go in the incinerator.
That 'eternity' inscribed with both their names is
his surety that they'd be together, 'later'.

I signed for the parcelled clothing as the son,
the cardy, apron, pants, bra, dress –

the clerk phoned down: *6-8-8-3-1?*
Has she still her ring on? (Slight pause) *Yes!*

It's on my warm palm now, your burnished ring!

I feel your ashes, head, arms, breasts, womb, legs,
sift through its circle slowly, like that thing
you used to let me watch to time the eggs.

Death Be Not Proud

from *Holy Sonnets (Divine Meditations)*

Death be not proud, though some have called thee
Mighty and dreadfull, for, thou are not soe,
For, those, whom thou think'st, thou dost overthrow,
Die not, poore death, nor yet canst thou kill mee;
From rest and sleepe, which but thy pictures bee,
Much pleasure, then from thee, much more must flow,
And soonest our best men with thee doe goe,
Rest of their bones, and soules deliverie.
Thou art slave to Fate, chance, kings, and desperate men,
And dost with poyson, warre, and sicknesse dwell,
And poppie, or charmes can make us sleepe as well,
And better then thy stroake; why swell'st thou then?
One short sleepe past, wee wake eternally,
And death shall be no more, death, thou shalt die.

Do Not

Do not go gentle into that good night,
Old age should burn and rave at close of day;
Rage, rage against the dying of the light.

Go

Though wise men at their end know dark is right,
Because their words had forked no lightning they
Do not go gentle into that good night.

Gentle

Good men, the last wave by, crying how bright
Their frail deeds might have danced in a green bay,
Rage, rage against the dying of the light.

into

Wild men who caught and sang the sun in flight,
And learn, too late, they grieved it on its way,
Do not go gentle into that good night.

That

Grave men, near death, who see with blinding sight
Blind eyes could blaze like meteors and be gay,
Rage, rage against the dying of the light.

Good

And you, my father, there on the sad height,
Curse, bless, me now with your fierce tears, I pray.
Do not go gentle into that good night.
Rage, rage against the dying of the light.

Night

News Desk

Poetry is packed with headlines that can make us think and heartlines that can make us feel. As it says in the **News Desk** programme, 'A shock report, out today, claims that poetry can give more insight into the news than print journalism or even radio and television.'

Dylan Thomas reminds us in the first poem in this section, 'The Hand that Signed the Paper', that so much suffering is caused by people, not just by accident. Paul Dehn's poem 'Gutter Press' uses the language of newspapers to put the press in perspective, whilst Adrian Mitchell reminds us of the pain that is so often behind the print, and warns us against wallowing in righteous indignation. The poem by James Simmons focuses on deadly incidents in Northern Ireland and the way they change or destroy ordinary lives.

The lives of ordinary people have always been at risk: some things never seem to change. That point is aptly made in an anonymous poem written hundreds of years ago in protest against the way in which the law helps the rich to steal from the poor. The language of officialdom is at the opposite extreme from the language of poetry: the former uses maximum words to say nothing, whilst the latter uses minimum words to say something. Raymond Wilson makes that point ironically in his poem which is in the form of an officially insensitive letter about the need to move out of the way before the motorway hits you.

There's nothing new about suffering either, and the ancient ballad of Sir Patrick Spens tells of the loss of a brave crew because of a royal hand that signed a paper.

People can be a problem for Benjamin Zephaniah, but not all people, and as a poet without a chip on his shoulder, he cheerfully declares, 'I am not de problem'. It is often said that no news is good news, but Valerie Bloom casts a wry black eye on the good news we don't often hear. Poems don't need to be long to be powerful.

A poet is never a voice in a vacuum. Poets live in a social context, but they also live in a literary context. Most writers are conscious of the literary traditions of which they are part, as in the next pair of poems, where one is written with deliberate echoes of the other. Henry Reed's famous poem of the Second World War 'The Naming of Parts' is saluted through Simon Rae's recent poem about the agonies of Bosnia.

Another poem which acknowledges the way that 'the radio's terrible news' enters our safe-seeming lives is Gillian Clarke's 'The Field-Mouse'. Her other two poems show a similar sense that we live in a world where we are all neighbours now, and Chernobyl proves it.

The final poem in this section contrasts with the published lies that are told and sold for profit. It is by Desanka Maksimović, a poet born in what was Yugoslavia, and it celebrates the lies that are spoken out of kindness.

The Hand
that Signed the Paper

DYLAN THOMAS

The hand that signed the paper felled a city;
Five sovereign fingers taxed the breath,
Doubled the globe of dead and halved a country;
These five kings did a king to death.

The mighty hand leads to a sloping shoulder,
The finger joints are cramped with chalk;
A goose's quill has put an end to murder
That put an end to talk.

The hand that signed the treaty bred a fever,
And famine grew, and locusts came;
Great is the hand that holds dominion over
Man by a scribbled name.

The five kings count the dead but do not soften
The crusted wound nor stroke the brow;
A hand rules pity as a hand rules heaven;
Hands have no tears to flow.

27

Gutter Press

News Editor: Peer Confesses,
Bishop Undresses,
Torso Wrapped in Rug,
Girl Guide Throttled,
Baronet Bottled,
J.P. Goes to Jug.

But yesterday's story's
Old and hoary.
Never mind who got hurt.
No use grieving,
Let's get weaving.
What's the latest dirt?

Diplomat Spotted,
Scout Garrotted,
Thigh Discovered in Bog,
Wrecks Off Barmouth,

Sex in Yarmouth,
Woman In Love With Dog,
Eminent Hostess Shoots Her Guests,
Harrogate Lovebird Builds Two Nests.

Cameraman: *Builds two nests?*
              Shall I get a picture of the lovebird singing?
              Shall I get a picture of her pretty little eggs?
              Shall I get a picture of her babies?

News Editor: No!
              Go and get a picture of her legs.

              Beast Slays Beauty,
              Priest Flays Cutie,
              Cupboard Shows Tell-Tale Stain,
              Mate Drugs Purser,
              Dean Hugs Bursar,
              Mayor Binds Wife With Chain,
              Elderly Monkey Marries For Money,
              Jilted Junky Says 'I Want My Honey'.

Cameraman: *'Want my honey?'*
              Shall I get a picture of the pollen flying?
              Shall I get a picture of the golden dust?
              Shall I get a picture of a queen bee?

News Editor: No!
              Go and get a picture of her bust.

              Judge Gets Frisky,
              Nun Drinks Whisky,
              Baby Found Burnt in Cot,
              Show Girl Beaten,
              Duke Leaves Eton –

Cameraman: *Newspaper Man Gets Shot!*
              May all things clean
              And fresh and green
              Have mercy upon your soul,
              Consider yourself paid
              By the hole my bullet made –

News Editor: (dying) Come and get a picture of the
              hole.

Saw It In The Papers

ADRIAN MITCHELL

Her baby was two years old.
She left him, strapped in his pram, in the kitchen.
She went out.
She stayed with friends.
She went out drinking.

The baby was hungry.
Nobody came.
The baby cried.
Nobody came.
The baby tore at the upholstery of his pram.
Nobody came.

She told the police:
'I thought the neighbours would hear him crying,
and report it to someone who would come
and take him away.'

Nobody came.

The baby died of hunger.

She said she'd arranged for a girl,
whose name she couldn't remember,
to come and look after the baby
while she stayed with friends.
Nobody saw the girl.
Nobody came.

Her lawyer said there was no evidence
of mental instability.
But the man who promised to marry her
went off with another woman.

And when he went off, this mother changed
from a mother who cared for her two-year-old baby
into a mother who did not seem to care at all.
There was no evidence of mental instability.

The Welfare Department spokesman said:
'I do not know of any plans for an inquiry.
We never become deeply involved.'
Nobody came.
There was no evidence of mental instability.

When she was given love
She gave love freely to her baby.
When love was torn away from her
she locked her love away.
It seemed that no one cared for her.
She seemed to stop caring.
Nobody came.
There was no evidence of mental instability.

Only love can unlock locked-up-love.

Manslaughter: She pleaded Guilty.
She was sentenced to be locked up
in prison for four years.

Is there any love in prisons?

She must have been in great pain.

There is love in prisons.
There is great love in prisons.
A man in Gloucester Prison told me:
'Some of us care for each other.
Some of us don't.
Some of us are gentle,
Some are brutal.
All kinds.'

I said: 'Just the same as people outside.'
He nodded twice.
And stared me in the eyes.

What she did to him was terrible.
There was no evidence of mental instability.
What was done to her was terrible.
There is no evidence of mental instability.

Millions of children starve, but not in England.
What we do not do for them is terrible.

Is England's love locked up in England?
There is no evidence of mental instability.

Only love can unlock locked-up love.

Unlock all of your love.
You have enough for this woman.
Unlock all of your love.
You have enough to feed all those millions of children.

Cry if you like.
Do something if you can. You can.

JAMES SIMMONS

Claudy

for Harry Barton, a song

The Sperrins surround it, the Faughan flows by,
at each end of Main Street the hills and the sky,
the small town of Claudy at ease in the sun
last July in the morning, a new day begun.

How peaceful and pretty if the moment could stop,
McIlhenny is straightening things in his shop,
and his wife is outside serving petrol, and then
a girl takes a cloth to a big window pane.

And McCloskey is taking the weight off his feet,
and McClelland and Miller are sweeping the street,
and, delivering milk at the Beaufort Hotel,
young Temple's enjoying his first job quite well.

And Mrs McLaughlin is scrubbing her floor,
and Artie Hone's crossing the street to a door,
and Mrs Brown, looking around for her cat,
goes off up an entry – what's strange about that?

Not much – but before she comes back to the road
that strange car parked outside her house will explode,
and all of the people I've mentioned outside
will be waiting to die or already have died.

An explosion too loud for your eardrums to bear,
and young children squealing like pigs in the square,
and all faces chalk-white and streaked with bright red,
and the glass and the dust and the terrible dead.

For an old lady's legs are ripped off, and the head
of a man's hanging open, and still he's not dead.
He is screaming for mercy, and his son stands and stares
and stares, and then suddenly, quick, disappears.

And Christ, little Katherine Aiken is dead,
and Mrs McLaughlin is pierced through the head.
Meanwhile to Dungiven the killers have gone,
and they're finding it hard to get through on the phone.

The
Common
and the
Goose

The law locks up the man or woman
Who steals the goose from off the common
But leaves the greater felon loose
Who steals the common from the goose.

This Letter's to Say

Dear Sir or Madam,
This letter's to say
Your property
Stands bang in the way
Of Progress, and
Will be knocked down
On March the third
At half-past one.

There is no appeal,
Since the National Need
Depends on more
And still more Speed,
And this, in turn,
Dear Sir or Madam,
Depends on half England
Being tar-macadam.
(But your house will –
We are pleased to say –
Be the fastest lane
Of the Motorway).

Meanwhile the Borough
Corporation
Offer you new
Accommodation
Three miles away
On the thirteenth floor
(Flat Number Q
6824).

But please take note,
The Council regret:
No dog, cat, bird
Or other pet;
No noise permitted,
No singing in the bath
(For permits to drink
Or smoke or laugh
Apply on Form
Z 327);
No children admitted
Aged under eleven;
No hawkers, tramps
Or roof-top lunchers;
No opening doors
To Bible-punchers.

Failure to pay
Your rent, when due,
Will lead to our
Evicting you.
The Council demand
That you consent
To the terms above
When you pay your rent.

Meanwhile we hope
You will feel free
To consult us
Should there prove to be
The slightest case
Of difficulty.

With kind regards,
Yours faithfully ...

ANON

Sir
Patrick Spens

The king sits in Dumferling toune,
　　Drinking the blude-reid wine:
O whar will I get guid sailor,
　　To sail this schip of mine?

Up and spak an eldern knicht,
　　Sat at the kings richt kne:
Sir Patrick Spens is the best sailor
　　That sails upon the se.

The king has written a braid letter,
　　And signed wi his hand,
And sent it to Sir Patrick Spens,
　　Was walking on the sand.

The first line that Sir Patrick red,
    A loud lauch lauched he;
The next line that Sir Patrick red,
    The teir blinded his ee.

O wha is this has done this deid,
    This ill deid don to me,
To send me out this time o the yeir,
    To sail upon the se?

Mak hast, mak hast, my mirry men all,
    Our guid schip sails the morne:
O say na sae, my master deir,
    For I feir a deadlie storme.

Late late yestreen I saw the new moone,
    Wi the auld moone in hir arme,
And I feir, I feir, my deir master,
    That we will cum to harme.

O our Scots nobles were richt laith
    To weet their cork-heild schoone;
Bot lang owre a' the play wer playd,
    Thair hats they swam aboone.

O lang, lang, may their ladies sit,
    Wi thair fans into their hand,
Or eir they se Sir Patrick Spens
    Cum sailing to the land.

O lang, lang, may the ladies stand,
    Wi thair gold kems in their hair,
Waiting for their ain deir lords,
    For they'll se thame na mair.

Have owre, have owre to Aberdour,
    It's fifty fadom deip,
And thair lies guid Sir Patrick Spens,
    Wi the Scots lords at his feit.

braid	long
laith	loath
aboone	above (them)
Have owre	Half over

No Problem

I am not de problem
But I bare de brunt
Of silly playground taunts
An racist stunts,
I am not de problem
I am a born academic
But dey got me on de run
Now I am branded athletic,
I am not de problem
If yu give I a chance
I can teach yu of Timbuktu
I can do more dan dance,
I am not de problem
I greet yu wid a smile
Yu put me in a pigeon hole
But I am versatile.

These conditions may affect me
As I get older,
An I am positively sure
I hav no chips on me shoulders,
Black is not de problem
Mother country get it right,
An jus fe de record,
Sum of me best friends are white.

Yuh Hear Bout?

Yuh hear bout di people dem arres
Fi bun dung di Asian people dem house?
Yuh hear bout di policeman dem lock up
Fi beat up di black bwoy widout a cause?
Yuh hear bout di M.P. dem sack because im refuse fi help
im black constituents in a dem fight 'gainst deportation?
Yuh noh hear bout dem?
Me neida.

Lessons of the War

Naming of Parts

Today we have naming of parts. Yesterday,
We had daily cleaning. And tomorrow morning,
We shall have what to do after firing. But today,
Today we have naming of parts. Japonica
Glistens like coral in all of the neighbouring gardens,
      And today we have naming of parts.

This the lower sling swivel. And this
Is the upper sling swivel, whose use you will see,
When you are given your slings. And this is the piling swivel,
Which in your case you have not got. The branches
Hold in the gardens their silent, eloquent gestures,
      Which in our case we have not got.

This is the safety-catch, which is always released
With an easy flick of the thumb. And please do not let me
See anyone using his finger. You can do it quite easy
If you have any strength in your thumb. The blossoms
Are fragile and motionless, never letting anyone see
      Any of them using their finger.

And this you can see is the bolt. The purpose of this
Is to open the breech, as you see. We can slide it
Rapidly backwards and forwards: we call this
Easing the spring. And rapidly backwards and forwards
The early bees are assaulting and fumbling the flowers:
      They call it easing the Spring.

They call it easing the Spring: it is perfectly easy
If you have any strength in your thumb: like the bolt,
And the breech, and the cocking-piece, and the point of balance,
Which in our case we have not got; and the almond-blossom
Silent in all of the gardens and the bees going backwards
   and forwards,
      For today we have naming of parts.

Lessons of the War

(*after*

Henry

Reed)

SIMON RAE

*As the 1992 Olympics got underway, thousands of
Bosnians were being put in concentration camps.*

Today we have breaking of hearts. Yesterday
We had ethnic cleansing. And tomorrow morning
We shall have what to do after firing the village.
But today we have breaking of hearts. Refugees
Queue at the borders of all of the neighbouring countries,
    And today we have breaking of hearts.

This is the latest agreement, whose purpose
Is beating the clock. Insurgents go rapidly backwards
And forwards assaulting and torching the houses.
They call it re-writing the record. And athletes
Go rapidly backwards and forwards, beat.ng the clock
    In order to re-write the records.

This is your sports field today. And this
Is the long-jump pit whose use you will quickly discover
If we hear anyone singing a national anthem
Or wanting the toilet. Anthems are played by the band
(Who've been to the toilet) for every flag on the flagpole.
    Which in our case we have not got.

41

Summer, and the long grass is a snare drum.
The air hums with jets.
Down at the end of the meadow,
far from the radio's terrible news,
we cut the hay. All afternoon
its wave breaks before the tractor blade.
Over the hedge our neighbour travels his field
in a cloud of lime, drifting our land
with a chance gift of sweetness.

The child comes running through the killed flowers,
his hands a nest of quivering mouse,
its black eyes two sparks burning.
We know it will die and ought to finish it off.
It curls in agony big as itself
and the star goes out in its eye.
Summer in Europe, the fields hurt,
and the children kneel in long grass,
staring at what we have crushed.

Before day's done the field lies bleeding,
the dusk garden inhabited by the saved, voles,
frogs, a nest of mice. The wrong that woke
from a rumour of pain won't heal,
and we can't face the newspapers.
All night I dream the children dance in grass
their bones brittle as mouse-ribs, the air
stammering with gunfire, my neighbour turned
stranger, wounding my land with stones.

The
Field ~Mouse

S
u
n
d
a
y

Getting up early on a Sunday morning
leaving them sleep for the sake of peace,
the lunch pungent, windows open
for a blackbird singing in Cyncoed.
Starlings glistening in the gutter come
for seed. I let the cats in from the night,
their fur already glossed and warm with March.
I bring the milk, newspaper, settle here
in the bay of the window to watch people
walking to church for Mothering Sunday.
A choirboy holds his robes over his shoulder.
The cats jump up on windowsills to wash
and tremble at the starlings. Like peaty water
sun slowly fills the long brown room.
Opening the paper I admit to this
the war-shriek and starved stare
of a warning I can't name.

43

Neighbours

That spring was late. We watched the sky
and studied charts for shouldering isobars.
Birds were late to pair. Crows drank from the lamb's eye.

Over Finland small birds fell: song-thrushes
steering north, smudged signatures on light,
migrating warblers, nightingales.

Wing-beats failed over fjords, each lung a sip of gall.
Children were warned of their dangerous beauty.
Milk was spilt in Poland. Each quarrel

the blowback from some old story,
a mouthful of bitter air from the Ukraine
brought by the wind out of its box of sorrows.

This spring a lamb sips caesium on a Welsh hill.
A child, lifting her face to drink the rain,
takes into her blood the poisoned arrow.

Now we are all neighbourly, each little town
in Europe twinned to Chernobyl, each heart
with the burnt fireman, the child on the Moscow train.

In the democracy of the virus and the toxin
we wait. We watch for bird migrations,
one bird returning with green in its voice,

glasnost,
golau glas*,
a first break of blue.

golau glas   blue light

For Lies Spoken out of Kindness

Translated by Vasa D. Mihailovich

I seek mercy
for those who lack the courage
to tell the evil one that he is evil
or the bad one that he is bad,
for those who hesitate
to hurt with the truth,
for the people who lie out of kindness.
For the man who would rather be humiliated
than humiliate,
for the man who has no heart
to pull down a mask when he sees it
on someone's face,
for people who cannot insult
those of different thoughts and creeds,
for those who never could
pronounce a sentence to others,
for whom all judges seem strict,
for every kind untruthful story
and other similar weaknesses.

45

I Tell You I Don't Love You

Love makes the words go round – you can tell that from the number of love poems and songs that there are and always have been. This section starts with Annette O'Boyle's poem 'I Tell You I Don't Love You', which is a useful reminder that you can't always believe what lovers seem to say. Liz Lochhead enjoys teasing us as readers. She raps out her thoughts on the idea of not thanking her lover for a valentine because she's had enough of clichés and claptrap, but keeps her surprise for the end. This is followed by two poems from John Cooper Clarke, giving a male point of view on this loving business.

The language of love is a language of comparisons, none more famous than Shakespeare's comparison of his beloved to a summer's day. Following it is 'A Summer's Day' by Tom Leonard which must be one of the best examples of anti-poetry around: instead of the elegant eloquence of Shakespeare's sonnet he offers us the stumbling incoherence of love in real life, when the words just won't reach.

Kathleen Raine's 'Amo Ergo Sum' reminds us that we live because we love and John Donne's poem 'The Flea' is a wickedly witty defence of love bites. Then come the three poems by Grace Nichols, the featured poet in this section. She knows that love can burn as brightly as a flame, but she manages to laugh about love too, as in the poem 'The Fat Black Woman's Instructions to a Suitor'. In her third poem she offers us a taste of the food of love along with the reminder that we need to 'keep to de motion of we own person/ality'.

Love is about loss as well as laughter: W. H. Auden knew that the man he loved was dead, and in his 'Song' he laments that he was wrong to think that love would last for ever. One of the most famous poems in this section is 'La Belle Dame Sans Merci' by John Keats. At least the setting matches the mood when 'the sedge is withered from the lake and no birds sing'. In the contrasting context provided by Dennis O'Driscoll's poem set in a supermarket, 'Misunderstanding and Muzak', it's embarrassing to be alone and palely loitering down the aisles, rather than the aisle. A reminder that love springs eternal in the well-fed human breast comes from the anonymous poet who was in love with Sally at the chop-house.

It's not always love at first sight with poems, and the two final poems repay re-readings. The first is 'Mirrors' by Elizabeth Jennings and the second is by E. E. Cummings whose poetic voice, like his use of punctuation, is intriguingly individual. His poem 'somewhere i have never travelled,gladly beyond' reminds us that we read poems as we read the experience of love, in ways that no-one else can ever totally share.

I Tell You

I Don't Love You

ANNETTE O'BOYLE

I tell you 'I don't love you,
I don't know you well enough.'
I tell you 'I don't care for
          you at all'
And all that stuff.
I know you think I mean it,
Though I don't sound too sincere,
When I tell you you mean nothing
To me, even when you're near.
I tell you all these things
          to try
To make you understand,
That I don't want to kiss you,
Or even hold your hand,
That I don't get one bit jealous
When another flirts with you.
I tell you 'I don't love you'
But I do.

47

I Wouldn't Thank You for a Valentine

(Rap)

I wouldn't thank you for a Valentine.
I won't wake up early wondering if the postman's been.
Should 10 red-padded satin hearts arrive with a sticky sickly
        saccharine
Sentiments in very vulgar verses I wouldn't wonder if you
        meant them.
Two dozen anonymous Interflora roses?
I'd not bother to swither over who sent them!
I wouldn't thank you for a Valentine.

Scrawl SWALK across the envelope
I'd just say "Same Auld Story
I canny be bothered deciphering it –
I'm up to here with Amore!
The whole Valentine's Day Thing is trivial and commercial,
A cue for unleashing clichés and candyheart motifs to which I
      personally am not partial."
Take more than singing Telegrams, or pints of Chanel Five,
      or sweets,
To get me ordering oysters or ironing my black satin sheets.
I wouldn't thank you for a Valentine.

If you sent me a solitaire and promises solemn,
Took out an ad in the Guardian Personal Column
Saying something very soppy such as "Who Loves Ya, Poo?
I'll tell you, I do, Fozzy Bear, that's who!"
You'd entirely fail to charm me, in fact I'd detest it
I wouldn't be eighteen again for anything, I'm glad I'm past it.
I wouldn't thank you for a Valentine.

If you sent me a single orchid, or a pair of Janet Reger's in a
      heart-shaped box and declared your Love Eternal
I'd say I'd not be caught dead in them they were politically
      suspect and I'd rather something thermal.
If you hired a plane and blazed our love in a banner across the
      skies;
If you bought me something flimsy in a flatteringly wrong size;
If you sent me a postcard with three Xs and told me how you
      felt
I wouldn't thank you, I'd melt.

i wanna be yours

let me be your vacuum cleaner
breathing in your dust
let me be your ford cortina
i will never rust
if you like your coffee hot
let me be your coffee pot
you call the shots
i wanna be yours

let me be your raincoat
for those frequent rainy days
let me be your dreamboat
when you wanna sail away
let me be your teddy bear
take me with you anywhere
i don't care
i wanna be yours

let me be your electric meter
i will not run out
let me be the electric heater
you get cold without
let me be your setting lotion
hold your hair
with deep devotion
deep as the deep
atlantic ocean
that's how deep is my emotion
deep deep deep deep de deep deep
i don't wanna be hers
i wanna be yours

 the Business?

Does Superman wear blue tights?
And keep away from kryptonite?
Do old ladies get mugged at night?
R U the Business?

Do workers want a living wage?
Do rock stars lie about their age?
Would a tiger run from an open cage?
R U the Business?

Is my first name John?
Is Strangeways full of prisoners?
Am I over 21?

Are the Royal Family rich?
Was Scooby Doo one son of a bitch?
Is Wembley Stadium a football pitch?
R U the Business?

Did Noriega knock out coke?
Did Bob Marley like the odd smoke?
Was Jesus Christ a decent bloke?
R U the Business?

Does Oliver Reed ever get pissed?
Can Chubby Checker do the Twist?
Was Karl Marx a communist?
R U the Business?

Was James Dean a cool cat?
Was Kennedy a Democrat?
Do Hassidic men wear hats?
R U the Business?

Will narcotics get you hooked?
Did Dostoyevsky write the odd book?
Was Al Capone a bit of a crook?
R U the Business?

Did Elvis ever rock 'n' roll?
Does James Brown have any soul?
Would I touch you with a ten-foot barge pole?
R U the Business?

Shall I Compare Thee to a Summer's Day?

Shall I compare thee to a summer's day?
Thou art more lovely and more temperate:
Rough winds do shake the darling buds of May,
And summer's lease hath all too short a date:
Sometime too hot the eye of heaven shines,
And often is his gold complexion dimmed;
And every fair from fair sometimes declines,
By chance or nature's changing course untrimmed;
But thy eternal summer shall not fade,
Nor lose possession of that fair thou owest;
Nor shall death brag thou wander'st in his shade,
When in eternal lines to time thou growest:
    So long as men can breathe, or eyes can see,
    So long lives this, and this gives life to thee.

A Summer's Day

yir eyes ur
eh
a mean yir

pirrit this wey
ah a thingk yir
byewtifl like ehm

fact
fact a thingk yir
ach a luvyi thahts

thahts
jist thi wey it iz like
thahts ehm
aw ther iz ti say

A
m
o

E
r
g
o

S
u
m

Because I love
> The sun pours out its rays of living gold
> Pours out its gold and silver on the sea.

Because I love
> The earth upon her astral spindle winds
> Her ecstasy-producing dance.

Because I love
> Clouds travel on the winds through wide skies,
> Skies wide and beautiful, blue and deep.

Because I love
> Wind blows white sails,
> The wind blows over flowers, the sweet wind blows.

Because I love
> The ferns grow green, and green the grass, and green
> The transparent sunlit trees.

Because I love
> Larks rise up from the grass
> And all the leaves are full of singing birds.

Because I love
> The summer air quivers with a thousand wings,
> Myriads of jewelled eyes burn in the light.

Because I love
> The iridescent shells upon the sand
> Take forms as fine and intricate as thought.

Because I love
> There is an invisible way across the sky,
> Birds travel by that way, the sun and moon
> And all the stars travel that path by night.

Because I love
> There is a river flowing all night long.

Because I love
> All night the river flows into my sleep,
> Ten thousand living things are sleeping in my arms,
> And sleeping wake, and flowing are at rest.

l e a
F
e
h
T

Marke but this flea, and marke in this,
How little that which thou deny'st me is;
It suck'd me first, and now sucks thee,
And in this flea, our two bloods mingled bee;
Thou know'st that this cannot be said
A sinne, nor shame, nor loss of maidenhead,
　　Yet this enjoyes before it wooe,
　　And pamper'd swells with one blood made of two
　　And this, alas, is more then wee would doe.

Oh stay, three lives in one flea spare,
Where wee almost, yea more then maryed are.
This flea is you and I, and this
Our mariage bed, and mariage temple is;
Though parents grudge, and you, w'are met,
And cloystered in these living walls of Jet.
　　Though use make you apt to kill mee,
　　Let not to that, selfe murder added bee,
　　And sacrilege, three sinnes in killing three.

Cruell and sodaine, hast thou since
Purpled thy naile, in blood of innocence?
Wherein could this flea guilty bee,
Except in that drop which it suckt from thee?
Yet thou triumph'st, and saist that thou
Find'st not thy selfe, nor mee the weaker now;
　　'Tis true, then learne how false, feares bee;
　　Just so much honor, when thou yeeld'st to mee,
　　Will wast, as this flea's death tooke life from thee.

55

Like a Flame

Raising up
from my weeding
of ripening cane

my eyes
make four
with this man

there ain't
no reason
to laugh

but
I laughing
in confusion

his hands
soft his words
quick his lips
curling as in
prayer

I nod

I like this man

Tonight
I go to meet him
like a flame

The Fat Black Woman's Instructions to a Suitor

Do the boggie-woggie
Do the hop
Do the Charlestown
Do the rock
Do the chicken funky
Do the foxtrot

Do the tango
Drop yourself like a mango
Do the minuet
Spin me a good ole pirouette
Do the highland fling
Get down baby
Do that limbo thing

After doing all that, and maybe mo
hope you have a little energy left
to carry me across the threshold

even Tho

Man I love
but won't let you devour

even tho
I'm all watermelon
and starapple and plum
when you touch me

even tho
I'm all seamoss
and jellyfish
and tongue

Come
leh we go to de carnival
You be banana
I be avocado

Come
leh we hug up
and brace-up
and sweet one another up

But then
leh we break free
yes, leh we break free

And keep to de motion
of we own person/ality

Song

Stop all the clocks, cut off the telephone,
Prevent the dog from barking with a juicy bone,
Silence the pianos and with muffled drum
Bring out the coffin, let the mourners come.

Let aeroplanes circle moaning overhead
Scribbling on the sky the message He Is Dead,
Put crêpe bows round the white necks of the public doves,
Let the traffic policemen wear black cotton gloves.

He was my North, my South, my East and West,
My working week and my Sunday rest,
My noon, my midnight, my talk, my song;
I thought that love would last for ever: I was wrong.

The stars are not wanted now: put out every one;
Pack up the moon and dismantle the sun;
Pour away the ocean and sweep up the wood.
For nothing now can ever come to any good.

from *Twelve Songs, IX*

La Belle Dame

Dame

Sans Merci

O what can ail thee, knight-at-arms,
    Alone and palely loitering?
The sedge is withered from the lake,
    And no birds sing.

O what can ail thee, knight-at-arms!
    So haggard and so woe-begone?
The squirrel's granary is full,
    and the harvest's done.

I see a lily on thy brow
    With anguish moist and fever dew,
And on thy cheek a fading rose
    Fast withereth too.

I met a lady in the meads,
    Full beautiful – a faery's child,
Her hair was long, her foot was light,
    And her eyes were wild.

I made a garland for her head,
    And bracelets too, and fragrant zone;
She looked at me as she did love,
    And made sweet moan.

I set her on my pacing steed,
    And nothing else saw all day long,
For sidelong would she bend, and sing
    A faery's song.

She found me roots of relish sweet,
    And honey wild, and manna dew,
And sure in language strange she said –
    'I love thee true.'

She took me to her elfin grot,
        And there she wept, and sighed full sore.
And there I shut her wild, wild eyes
        With kisses four.

And there she lulled me asleep,
        And there I dreamed – Ah! woe betide!
The latest dream I ever dreamed
        On the cold hill side.

I saw pale kings and princes too,
        Pale warriors, death-pale were they all;
They cried – 'La Belle Dame sans Merci
        Hath thee in thrall!'

I saw their starved lips in the gloam,
        With horrid warning gaped wide,
And I awoke and found me here,
        On the cold hill side.

And this is why I sojourn here,
        Alone and palely loitering,
Though the sedge is withered from the lake,
        And no birds sing.

DENNIS O'DRISCOLL

M^iS_un^de_r^st^an^d^in^g and M^uZak

You are in the Super Valu supermarket
expecting to meet me at 6.15.

I am in the Extra Valu supermarket
expecting to meet you at 6.15.

Danny Boy is calling you down special-offer aisles.
Johann Strauss is waltzing me down special-offer aisles.

I weigh mushrooms and broccoli and beans.
You weigh beans and mushrooms and broccoli.

62

It is 6.45. No sign of you.
It is 6.45. No sign of me.

You may have had a puncture.
I may have been held up at work.

It is 6.55. You may have been murdered.
It is 6.55. I may have been flattened by a truck.

Danny Boy starts crooning all over you again.
Johann Strauss starts dancing all over me again.

Everything that's needed for our Sunday lunch
is heaped up in my trolley, your trolley.

We hope to meet somewhere, to eat it.

To Sally, at the Chop-House

Dear Sally, emblem of the chop-house ware,
As broth reviving, and as white bread fair;
As small beer grateful, and as pepper strong,
As beef-steak tender, as fresh pot-herbs young;
Sharp as a knife, and piercing as a fork,
Soft as new butter, white as fairest pork;
Sweet as young mutton, brisk as bottled beer,
Smooth as is oil, juicy as cucumber,
And bright as cruet void of vinegar.
O Sally! could I turn and shift my love
With the same skill that you your steaks can move,
My heart, thus cooked, might prove a chop-house feast,
And you alone should be the welcome guest.
But, dearest Sal, the flames that you impart,
Like chop on gridiron, broil my tender heart!
Which, if thy kindly helping hand be n't nigh,
Must, like an up-turned chop, hiss, brown and fry;
And must at last, thou scorcher of my soul,
Shrink, and become an undistinguished coal.

ANON

63

Mirrors

Was it a mirror then across a room,
A crowded room of parties where the smoke
Rose to the ceiling with the talk? The glass
Stared back at me a half-familiar face
Yet something hoped for. When at last you came
It was as if the distant mirror spoke.

That loving ended as all self-love ends
And teaches us that only fair-grounds have
The right to show us halls of mirrors where
In every place we look we see our stare
Taunting our own identities. But love
Perceives without a mirror in the hands.

somewhere i have never travelled,gladly beyond
any experience,your eyes have their silence:
in your most frail gesture are things which enclose me,
or which i cannot touch because they are too near

your slightest look easily will unclose me
though i have closed myself as fingers,
you open always petal by petal myself as Spring opens
(touching skilfully,mysteriously) her first rose

or if your wish be to close me,i and
my life will shut very beautifully,suddenly,
as when the heart of this flower imagines
the snow carefully everywhere descending;

nothing which we are to perceive in this world equals
the power of your intense fragility:whose texture
compels me with the colour of its countries,
rendering death and forever with each breathing

(i do not know what it is about you that closes
and opens;only something in me understands
the voice of your eyes is deeper than all roses)
nobody,not even the rain,has such small hands

65

Going Places

Every poem is an invitation to travel. We hope that the poet will take us somewhere worth visiting in the country of the imagination. The first poet in this section, Mike Kivi, takes us via a school English assignment into the terrifying, tantalising territory of a teenage holiday.

Some of the uncertainties we feel as travellers are linked with language, and the different words we use for food form the focus of a poem by Valerie Bloom. Derek Walcott recreates in words what 'Midsummer, Tobago' is like. As it says in the television programme, 'if you want a real sense of the place – the atmosphere, the mood, the way people there think and feel, the dreams they dream – you need a poem' not a tourist board poster. It is followed by U. A. Fanthorpe's 'First Flight', a poem with many voices, some of them those of contemporary travellers but one an echo of that first flight ever, which took Icarus too near the sun on his feathered wings.

'Buffaloes' by Sujata Bhatt is a powerful evocation of the atmosphere and the voices of India. This is followed by Simon Armitage's poem 'The Metaphor Now Standing at Platform 8', which reminds us that life is not a destination but a journey. Keith Douglas in his 'Behaviour of Fish in an Egyptian Tea Garden' suggests that the predators of the deep have their human equivalents, especially where sex is concerned. His poem offers a rich harvest of images and after reading it neither cafeteria nor aquaria are likely to be the same again.

John Agard offers us a dissertation on palm trees and a lesson in learning not to think in stereotypes. His second poem 'First black man in space' is in a similar vein: it includes a surprise meeting with God, who proves to be black and a woman. Seeing ourselves as others from outer space might see us is the starting point of Craig Raine's 'A Martian Sends a Postcard Home', in which the ordinary is made extraordinary.

What you see naturally depends on how you do your looking. Dragons have tended to have a bad press over the years, but U. A. Fanthorpe's poem 'Not My Best Side' gives us a dragon's-eye view of a mythical conflict, inspired by Uccello's painting in the National Gallery. Shelley's 'Ozymandias' puts things in historical perspective: his meeting with a traveller from an antique land shows how ordinary the supposedly extraordinary becomes with the passage of time.

The three final poems in this section are by the featured poet Seamus Heaney. The first, 'The Plantation', is about a solidly geographical place, but one in which you can learn how to lose yourself. The other two are about places deep inside where you can learn how to find yourself by passing through the Frontier of Writing or visiting the Republic of Conscience.

September
Assignment

Write about 500 words on one of the following:
- i)   *My summer holiday*
- ii)   *Adolescent relationships*
- iii) *Pop Music*

Deep in the heat of a camp site rave,
Little Tina Turnbull dances the night,
Filled with the thrill of a chemical wave,
Flying in the flash of fluorescent light.
Driven by the rhythm of a high speed laser,
Pulse pumped hard with a pocket full of pills,
High as a kite, sharp as a razor,
Stuttering steps in the strobe light stills.
Boogying close as the beat drives harder,
Hippity together to the disco door,
Sinking in the seat of a clapped out Lada,
Scrabbling for the condoms on the cold car floor.
Back to the caravan at half past three
(Parents paralytic on the double divan)
Worried over syphilis and HIV,
Pimples that appeared instead of a tan.
Packed next morning sitting in the car,
Eyes shut tight with her walkman on,
Dreams of a foetus in a marmalade jar,
Childhood, babies, holidays gone.
Rainclouds form on the fading hill,
Wipers start to squeak on the fly-stained screen,
Eyes turned cold in the wintry chill
As the radio plays sweet little sixteen.

67

Wha Fe Call I'

Miss Ivy, tell mi supmn,
An mi wan' yuh ansa good.
When yuh eat roun 12 o'clock,
Wassit yuh call yuh food?

For fram mi come yah mi confuse,
An mi noh know which is right,
Weddah dinnah a de food yuh eat midday,
Or de one yuh eat a night.

Mi know sey breakfus a de mawnin one,
But cyan tell ef suppa a six or t'ree,
An one ting mi wi nebba undastan,
Is when yuh hab yuh tea.

Miss A dung a London ha lunch 12 o'clock,
An dinnah she hab bout t'ree,
Suppa she hab bout six o'clock,
But she noh hab noh tea.

Den mi go a Cambridge todda day,
Wi hab dinnah roun' bout two,
T'ree hour later mi frien she sey,
Mi hungry, how bout yuh?

Joe sey im tink a suppa time,
An mi sey yes, mi agree,
She halla, 'Suppa? a five o'clock,
Missis yuh mussa mean tea!'

Den Sunday mi employer get up late,
Soh she noh hab breakfus nor lunch,
But mi hear she a talk bout 'Elevenses'
An one sinting dem call 'Brunch'.

Breakfus, elevenses, an brunch,
lunch, dinnah, suppa, tea,
Mi brain cyan wuk out which is which,
An when a de time fe hab i'.

For jus' when mi mek headway,
Sinting dreadful set mi back,
An dis when mi tink mi know dem all,
Mi hear bout one name snack.

Mi noh tink mi a badda wid no name,
Mi dis a nyam when time mi hungry,
For doah mi 'tomach wi glad fe de food,
I' couldn care less whey mi call i'.

Midsummer, Tobago

Broad sun-stoned beaches.

White heat.
A green river.

A bridge,
scorched yellow palms

from the summer-sleeping house
drowsing through August.

Days I have held,
days I have lost,

days that outgrow, like daughters,
my harbouring arms.

First Flight

Plane moves. I don't like the feel of it.
In a car I'd suspect low tyre pressure.

A sudden swiftness, earth slithers
Off at an angle. The experienced solidly

This is rather a short hop for me

Read *Guardians*, discuss secretaries,
Business lunches. I crane for the last of dear

I'm doing it just to say I've done it

Familiar England, motorways, reservoir,
Building sites. Nimble tiny-disc, a sun

Tell us when we get to water

Runs up the porthole and vanishes.
Under us the broad meringue kingdom

The next lot of water'll be the Med

Of cumulus, bearing the crinkled tangerine stain
That light spreads on an evening sea at home.

You don't need an overcoat, but
It's the sort of place where you need
A pullover. Know what I mean?

We have come too high for history.
Where we are now deals only with tomorrow,
Confounds the forecasters, dismisses clocks.

My last trip was Beijing. Know where that is?
Beijing. Peking, you'd say. Three weeks there, I was.
Peking is wrong. If you've been there
You call it Beijing, like me. Go on, say it.

Mackerel wigs dispense the justice of air.
At this height nothing lives. Too cold. Too near the sun.

71

Buffaloes

The young widow
thinks she should have burned on
her husband's funeral pyre.
She could not, for her mother-in-law
insisted she raise the only son
of her only son.
The young widow sits outside
in the garden overlooking a large pond.
Out of the way, still untouchable, she suckles
her three-week-old son
and thinks she could live
for those hungry lips; live to let him grow
bigger than herself. Her dreams lie
lazily swishing their tails
in her mind like buffaloes
dozing, some with only nostrils showing
in a muddy pond.

Tails switch
to keep fat flies away,
and horns, as long as a man's hand, or longer
keep the boys, and their pranks away.
It is to the old farmer's tallest son
they give their warm yellowish milk.
He alone approaches: dark-skinned and naked
except for a white turban, a white loincloth.
He joins them in the pond,
greets each one with love:
"my beauty", "my pet" –
slaps water on their broad flanks
splashes more water on their dusty backs.
Ears get scratched, necks rubbed,
drowsy faces are splashed awake.
Now he prods them out of the mud
out of the water, begging loudly
"Come my beauty, come my pet, let us go!"
And the pond shrinks back
as the wide black buffaloes rise.

The young widow
walks from tree to tree,
newly opened leaves brush damp sweet smells
across her face. The infant's mouth sleeps
against her breast. Dreams stuck
inside her chest twitch
as she watches the buffaloes pass
too close to her house, up the steep road
to the dairy. The loud loving voice
of the farmer's son holds them steady
without the bite of any stick or whip.

The

Metaphor

Now Standing

at Platform 8

will separate at Birmingham New Street, and passengers
for the South West who sit for safety reasons in the rear carriages
will find themselves at Shit Creek Central without a paddle
or a valid ticket. No end of fancy talking will save them.

Parents and their children are today invited
to the engine of the metaphor, and may touch the dead man's
        handle.
Cow-catchers? Fried bacon on the footplateman's shovel?
        People,
please, this is 1990 not the Wild West.

You kids licking the tips of your pencils, I could talk
of the age of steam, riding the great Similitudes
into the record books. Take heart, a boy
could do worse than be a spotter of metaphors.

Here is the buffet car at the centre
of the metaphor, where hot buttered toast
and alcoholic beverages will certainly be mentioned.
In the next breath, lunch will be served.

This is not the allegorical boat train.
This is not the symbolic seaplane.
Madam, life is not a destination but a journey; sweet
that your friends should want to meet you there, but stupid.

Passengers, as part of our Transports of Delight programme
let me welcome this morning's poets. Beginning at the guard's van
they will troubadour the aisle reciting their short but engaging
        pieces.
Sir, I understand you have a reservation?

Feet off the seats, please. Lady, for the last time,
extinguish that cigarillo. This is a metaphor I'm running here
not a jamboree, and as soon as we get that straight
we're rolling. Till then, no one goes nowhere.

Behaviour of Fish in an Egyptian Tea Garden

As a white stone draws down the fish
she on the seafloor of the afternoon
draws down men's glances and their cruel wish
for love. Her red lip on the spoon

slips-in a morsel of ice-cream. Her hands
white as a shell, are submarine
fronds, sink with spread fingers, lean
along the table, carmined at the ends.

A cotton magnate, an important fish
with great eyepouches and a golden mouth
through the frail reefs of furniture swims out
and idling, suspended, stays to watch.

A crustacean old man clamped to his chair
sits near her and might coldly see
her charms through fissures where the eyes should be;
or else his teeth are parted in a stare.

Captain on leave, a lean dark mackerel,
lies in the offing, turns himself and looks
through currents of sound. The flat-eyed flatfish sucks
on a straw, staring from its repose, laxly.

And gallants in shoals swim up and lag,
circling and passing near the white attraction –
sometimes pausing, opening a conversation –
fish pause so to nibble or tug.

Now the ice-cream is finished, is
paid for. The fish swim off on business
and she sits alone at the table, a white stone
useless except to a collector, a rich man.

75

Palm Tree King

Because I come from the West Indies
certain people in England seem to think
I is a expert on palm trees

So not wanting to sever dis link
with me native roots (know what ah mean?)
or to disappoint dese culture vulture
I does smile cool as seabreeze

and say to dem
which specimen
you interested in
cause you talking
to the right man
I is palm tree king
I know palm tree history
like de palm o me hand
In fact me navel string
bury under a palm tree

If you think de queen could wave
you ain't see nothing yet
till you see the Roystonea Regia
– that is the royal palm –
with she crown of leaves
waving calm-calm
over the blue Caribbean carpet
nearly 100 feet of royal highness

But let we get down to business
Tell me what you want to know
How tall a palm tree does grow?
What is the biggest coconut I ever see?
What is the average length of the leaf?

Don't expect me to be brief
cause palm tree history
is a long-long story

Anyway why you so interested
in length and circumference?
That kind of talk so ordinary
That don't touch the essence
of palm tree mystery
That is no challenge
to a palm tree historian like me

If you insist on statistics
why you don't pose a question
with some mathematical profundity?

Ask me something more tricky
like if a American tourist with a camera
take 9 minutes to climb a coconut tree
how long a English tourist without a camera
would take to climb the same coconut tree?

That is problem pardner
Now ah coming harder

If 6 straw hat
and half a dozen bikini
multiply by the same number of coconut tree
equal one postcard
how many square miles of straw hat
you need to make a tourist industry?

That is problem pardner
Find the solution
and you got a revolution

But before you say anything
let I palm tree king
give you dis warning
Ah want de answer in metric
it kind of rhyme with tropic
Besides it sound more exotic

First black man in
s   p   a   c   e

Afro-Cuban cosmonaut, 38-year-old Arnaldo
Tamayo Mendez, became the first black man in
space as part of the two-man crew of the USSR
space craft, SOYUZ 38. (From a news release
in Caribbean Contact, *October1980.)*

Others before him had gone
and come back
with their token
of moonrock
had planted their flag
and spoken
of the absence of gravity
the lightness of the body
that strange-dimensional sensation
of a spacesuit foetus
floating on moondust
a goldfish capsuled
in a galactic aquarium
with possible pebbles of uranium

But no one had prepared him for this
the booklets and leaflets
had said nothing of this
No the intensive briefing
had not prepared him for a meeting
with God face to face.
The press had hailed him
a national hero
an honour to the nation
a first for his race
a revolutionary breakthrough
but of this not a single clue.
Nothing about meeting
with God face to face
in outer space

Not one word
that God would be black
moreso a woman
and would greet him
not with a coke and hamburger
saying 'Geewhizz guy you made it'
but would embrace him
as a long-lost brother
of her race
would utter his name
offering him a cup
of maté tea
after the long journey
would say 'Compañero
a la luna bienvenido'

Wait till this gets back
to Moscow
or worse still Cape Canaveral

They won't believe the satellite photo

A Martian Sends a Postcard Home

Caxtons are mechanical birds with many wings
and some are treasured for their markings –

they cause the eyes to melt
or the body to shriek without pain.

I have never seen one fly, but
sometimes they perch on the hand.

Mist is when the sky is tired of flight
and rests its soft machine on ground:

then the world is dim and bookish
like engravings under tissue paper.

Rain is when the earth is television.
It has the property of making colours darker.

Model T is a room with the lock inside –
a key is turned to free the world

for movement, so quick there is a film
to watch for anything missed.

But time is tied to the wrist
or kept in a box, ticking with impatience.

In homes, a haunted apparatus sleeps,
that snores when you pick it up.

If the ghost cries, they carry it
to their lips and soothe it to sleep

with sounds. And yet, they wake it up
deliberately, by tickling with a finger.

Only the young are allowed to suffer
openly. Adults go to a punishment room

with water but nothing to eat.
They lock the door and suffer the noises

alone. No one is exempt
and everyone's pain has a different smell.

At night, when all the colours die,
they hide in pairs

and read about themselves –
in colour, with their eyelids shut.

Reproduced with kind permission of the National Gallery

St. George and the Dragon by Uccello

Not My Best Side

I

Not my best side, I'm afraid.
The artist didn't give me a chance to
Pose properly, and as you can see,
Poor chap, he had this obsession with
Triangles, so he left off two of my
Feet. I didn't comment at the time
(What, after all, are two feet
To a monster?) but afterwards
I was sorry for the bad publicity.
Why, I said to myself, should my conqueror
Be so ostentatiously beardless, and ride
A horse with a deformed neck and square hoofs?
Why should my victim be so
Unattractive as to be inedible,
And why should she have me literally
On a string? I don't mind dying
Ritually, since I always rise again,
But I should have liked a little more blood
To show they were taking me seriously.

II

It's hard for a girl to be sure if
She wants to be rescued. I mean, I quite
Took to the dragon. It's nice to be
Liked, if you know what I mean. He was
So nicely physical, with his claws
And lovely green skin, and that sexy tail,
And the way he looked at me,
He made me feel he was all ready to
Eat me. And any girl enjoys that.
So when this boy turned up, wearing machinery,
On a really *dangerous* horse, to be honest,
I didn't much fancy him. I mean,
What was he like underneath the hardware?
He might have acne, blackheads or even
Bad breath for all I could tell, but the dragon –
Well, you could see all his equipment
At a glance. Still, what could I do?
The dragon got himself beaten by the boy,
And a girl's got to think of her future.

III

I have diplomas in Dragon
Management and Virgin Reclamation.
My horse is the latest model, with
Automatic transmission and built-in
Obsolescence. My spear is custom-built,
And my prototype armour
Still on the secret list. You can't
Do better than me at the moment.
I'm qualified and equipped to the
Eyebrow. So why be difficult?
Don't you want to be killed and/or rescued
In the most contemporary way? Don't
You want to carry out the roles
That sociology and myth have designed for you?
Don't you realize that, by being choosy,
You are endangering job-prospects
In the spear- and horse-building industries?
What, in any case, does it matter what
You want? You're in my way.

Ozymandias

I met a traveller from an antique land
Who said: Two vast and trunkless legs of stone
Stand in the desert. Near them on the sand,
Half sunk, a shatter'd visage lies, whose frown
And wrinkled lip and sneer of cold command
Tell that its sculptor well those passions read
Which yet survive, stamp'd on these lifeless things,
The hand that mock'd them and the heart that fed;
And on the pedestal these words appear:
'My name is Ozymandias, king of kings:
Look on my works, ye Mighty, and despair!'
Nothing beside remains. Round the decay
Of that colossal wreck, boundless and bare,
The lone and level sands stretch far away.

The **P l a n t a t i o n**

Any point in that wood
Was a centre, birch trunks
Ghosting your bearings,
Improvising charmed rings

Wherever you stopped.
Though you walked a straight line
It might be a circle you travelled
With toadstools and stumps

Always repeating themselves.
Or did you re-pass them?
Here were blaeberries quilting the floor,
The black char of a fire

And having found them once
You were sure to find them again.
Someone had always been there
Though always you were alone.

Lovers, birdwatchers,
Campers, gipsies and tramps
Left some trace of their trades
Or their excrement.

Hedging the road so
It invited all comers
To the hush and the mush
Of its whispering treadmill,

Its limits defined,
So they thought, from outside.
They must have been thankful
For the hum of the traffic

If they ventured in
Past the picnickers' belt
Or began to recall
Tales of fog on the mountains.

You had to come back
To learn how to lose yourself,
To be pilot and stray – witch,
Hansel and Gretel in one.

From the Frontier of Writing

The tightness and the nilness round that space
when the car stops in the road, the troops inspect
its make and number and, as one bends his face

towards your window, you catch sight of more
on a hill beyond, eyeing with intent
down cradled guns that hold you under cover

and everything is pure interrogation
until a rifle motions and you move
with guarded unconcerned acceleration –

a little emptier, a little spent
as always by that quiver in the self,
subjugated, yes, and obedient.

So you drive on to the frontier of writing
where it happens again. The guns on tripods;
the sergeant with his on-off mike repeating

data about you, waiting for the squawk
of clearance; the marksman training down
out of the sun upon you like a hawk.

And suddenly you're through, arraigned yet freed,
as if you'd passed from behind a waterfall
on the black current of a tarmac road

past armour-plated vehicles, out between
the posted soldiers flowing and receding
like tree shadows into the polished windscreen.

From the Republic of Conscience

I When I landed in the republic of conscience
it was so noiseless when the engines stopped
I could hear a curlew high above the runway.

At immigration, the clerk was an old man
who produced a wallet from his homespun coat
and showed me a photograph of my grandfather.

The woman in customs asked me to declare
the words of our traditional cures and charms
to heal dumbness and avert the evil eye.

No porters. No interpreter. No taxi.
You carried your own burden and very soon
your symptoms of creeping privilege disappeared.

II Fog is a dreaded omen there but lightning
spells universal good and parents hang
swaddled infants in trees during thunderstorms.

Salt is their precious mineral. And seashells
are held to the ear during births and funerals.
The base of all inks and pigments is seawater.

Their sacred symbol is a stylized boat.
The sail is an ear, the mast a sloping pen,
The hull a mouth-shape, the keel an open eye.

At their inauguration, public leaders
must swear to uphold unwritten law and weep
to atone for their presumption to hold office –

and to affirm their faith that all life sprang
from salt in tears which the sky-god wept
after he dreamt his solitude was endless.

III I came back from that frugal republic
with my two arms the one length, the customs woman
having insisted my allowance was myself.

The old man rose and gazed into my face
and said that was official recognition
that I was now a dual citizen.

He therefore desired me when I got home
to consider myself a representative
and to speak on their behalf in my own tongue.

Their embassies, he said, were everywhere
but operated independently
and no ambassador would ever be relieved.

85

A Person is a Person

This section opens with Michael Rosen's poem for serious and sensible people who are grown-up enough to go out and have babies and to use that very special language, babytalk. This is followed by 'A Poem For A Very Special Person' – you, the reader. Further thoughts on growing up are offered by U. A. Fanthorpe, although she is aware of not having been too good at doing it herself. Unless you are careful, growing down into your second childhood of old age could be on the boring side. Better to take Jenny Joseph's advice and start practising now for when you are old and wear purple.

It is all too easy to forget that a person is a person and instead to start categorising people. In England the class game is often a language game, as Mary Casey suggests in her poem. Those who are members of the categorising tendency are John Agard's target in his poem 'Stereotype'. Poetry and prejudice don't sit too comfortably together because poetry is about the particular and prejudice has to be generalised.

The feeling that each person is uniquely valuable is reinforced in Simon Armitage's poem 'It Ain't What You Do It's What It Does To You'. History offers few better examples of that than the life of the writer of the next poem, John Clare. His poem 'I Am' was written in the asylum in which he spent the last 23 years of his life. This poem is followed by Auden's 'The Unknown Citizen' which depicts a bureaucratic society where nightmare normality undermines any individuality.

By contrast the next poem, 'Sho Nuff' by Nilene O. A. Foxworth, is full of personality, and the humour of Jim Wong-Chu's poem reminds us that since we are all equal in death, we should all be equal in life. In her poem 'The Choosing' Liz Lochhead, the featured poet, points out that our lives are often determined by decisions we never remember taking. Liz's personality shines through her poems with its honesty and humour: she knows what she is as a person, and, as she asserts in the 'What-I'm-Not Song', she knows what she isn't. She certainly isn't afraid of acknowledging the uncomfortable truth behind comforting clichés, and this is evident in her third poem 'The Visit'. Comparable honesty and anger are there in the poem 'In the Children's Hospital' by another Scots poet Hugh MacDiarmid.

The message that each person has the right to be a person is strong in the passionate questioning of Sojourner Truth as she demands 'Ain't I A Woman?' Gillian Clarke's poem 'My Box' reminds us that being loved ought to be a recognised human right, and the last poem of all, 'Remember?' by Alice Walker, ends with the twin flowers of justice and of hope.

We all need to begin by remembering that a person is a person: there is poetry in us all, and a voice that has the right to be visible.

When you're a
GROWN-UP...

When you're a GROWN-UP
a SERIOUS and SENSIBLE PERSON
When you've stopped being SILLY
you can go out and have babies
and go into a SERIOUS and SENSIBLE shop
and ask for:
Tuftytails, Paddipads, Bikkipegs, Cosytoes
and
Tommy Tippee Teethers.
Sno-bunnies, Visivents, Safeshines
Comfybaths, Dikkybibs
and
Babywipes.
Rumba Rattles and Trigger Jiggers
A Whirlee Three, a Finger Flip
or A Quacky Duck.
And if you're very SENSIBLE
you can choose
Easifitz, Babybuggies and a Safesitterstand.
Or is it a
Saferstandsit?
No it's a Sitstandsafe. I can never remember.
I'm sorry but Babytalk is a very difficult language.
It's for adults only.
Like 'X' films
Much too horrible for children.

A Poem For A

Listen
Will you do something for me?
Will you?
I want you to read this poem
Silently, carefully
And don't look surprised
When you find out
Who it's about.
Are you ready with your
'I'm not surprised' look?
Wait for it
This poem is about ...
> **YOU!**
>> **YES YOU!**

Well then, how does it feel
To have a poem written about you?
What d'you mean you don't like it?
Staring?
Of course they're all staring,
That's the whole point.
What's that?
You wish the poem had been about someone else?
I would have to pick on you, wouldn't I?
Look why not point back?
Make out it's one of them.
Go on. Point at somebody.
No, not him
Nobody would write a poem about him.

Very Special Person

Or her
Or ...
Well, maybe.
It's not working?
They're still staring?
You're not enjoying this too much, are you?
You see
That's another thing I know about you
You're one of those people
Who doesn't like
Having poems written about them.
Hurt? Me, hurt?
Of course I'm not hurt.

Poets are used to that sort of thing.
Tell you what. Here's a thought.
Just quietly, secretly
Close the book and
Slip it into your desk.
Wait!
Better still
Just leave it lying about
In a public place.

Someone is bound to pick it up
And think the poem is about them.
People are like that.

I wasn't good
At being a baby. Burrowed my way
Through the long yawn of infancy,
Masking by instinct how much I knew
Of the senior world, sabotaging
As far as I could, biding my time,
Biting my rattle, my brother (in private),
Shoplifting daintily into my pram.
Not a good baby,
No.

I wasn't good
At being a child. I missed
The innocent age. Children,
Being childish, were beneath me.
Adults I despised or distrusted. They
Would label my every disclosure
Precocious, naïve, whatever it was.
I disdained definition, preferred to be surly.
Not a nice child,
No.

I wasn't good
At adolescence. There was a dance,
A catchy rhythm; I was out of step.
My body capered, nudging me
With hairy, fleshy growths and monthly outbursts,
To join the party. I tried to annul
The future, pretended I knew it already,
Was caught bloody-thighed, a criminal
Guilty of puberty.
Not a nice girl,
No.

(My hero, intransigent Emily,
Cauterised her own-dog-mauled
Arm with a poker,
Struggled to die on her feet,
Never told anyone anything.)

growing up

I wasn't good
At growing up. Never learned
The natives' art of life. Conversation
Disintegrated as I touched it,
So I played mute, wormed along years,
Reciting the hard-learned arcane litany
Of cliché, my company passport.
Not a nice person,
No.

The gift remains
Masonic, dark. But age affords
A vocation even for wallflowers.
Called to be connoisseur, I collect,
Admire, the effortless bravura
Of other people's lives, proper and comely,
Treading the measure, shopping, chaffing,
Quarrelling, drinking, not knowing
How right they are, or how, like well-oiled bolts,
Swiftly and sweet, they slot into the grooves
Their ancestors smoothed out along the grain.

Warning

When I am an old woman I shall wear purple
With a red hat which doesn't go, and doesn't suit me.
And I shall spend my pension on brandy and summer gloves
And satin sandals, and say we've no money for butter.
I shall sit down on the pavement when I'm tired
And gobble up samples in shops and press alarm bells
And run my stick along the public railings
And make up for the sobriety of my youth.
I shall go out in my slippers in the rain
And pick the flowers in other people's gardens
And learn to spit.

You can wear terrible shirts and grow more fat
And eat three pounds of sausages at a go
Or only bread and pickle for a week
And hoard pens and pencils and beermats and things in boxes.

But now we must have clothes that keep us dry
And pay our rent and not swear in the street
And set a good example for the children.
We must have friends to dinner and read the papers.

But maybe I ought to practise a little now?
So people who know me are not too shocked and surprised
When suddenly I am old, and start to wear purple.

The Class Game

How can you tell what class I'm from?
I can talk posh like some
With an 'Olly in me mouth
Down me nose, wear an 'at not a scarf
With me second-hand clothes.
So why do you always wince when you hear
Me say 'Tara' to me 'Ma' instead of 'Bye Mummy
    dear'?
How can you tell what class I'm from?
'Cos we live in a corpy, not like some
In a pretty little semi, out Wirral way
And commute into Liverpool by train each day?
Or did I drop my unemployment card
Sitting on your patio (We have a yard)?
How can you tell what class I'm from?
Have I a label on me head, and another on me bum?
Or is it because my hands are stained with toil?
Instead of soft lily-white with perfume and oil?
Don't I crook me little finger when I drink me tea
Say toilet instead of bog when I want to pee?
Why do you care what class I'm from?
Does it stick in your gullet like a sour plum?
Well, mate! A cleaner is me mother
A docker is me brother
Bread pudding is wet nelly
And me stomach is me belly
And I'm proud of the class that I come from.

Stereotype

I'm a fullblooded
West Indian stereotype
You call me
happy-go-lucky
Yes that's me
dressing fancy
and chasing woman
if you think ah lie
bring yuh sister

I'm a fullblooded
West Indian stereotype
You wonder
where do you people
get such riddum
could it be the sunshine
My goodness
just listen to that steelband

Isn't there one thing
you forgot to ask
go on man ask ask
This native will answer anything
How about cricket?
I suppose you're good at it?
Hear this man
good at it!
Put de willow
in me hand
and watch me stripe
de boundary

Yes I'm a fullblooded
West Indian stereotype

that's why I
graduated from Oxford University
with a degree
in anthropology

I'm a fullblooded
West Indian stereotype
See me straw hat?
Watch it good

I'm a fullblooded
West Indian stereotype
You ask
if I got riddum
in me blood
You going ask!
Man just beat de drum
and don't forget
to pour de rum

I'm a fullblooded
West Indian stereotype
You say
I suppose you can show
us the limbo, can't you?
How you know!
How you know!
You sure
you don't want me
sing you a calypso too
How about that

It Ain't What You Do It's What It Does To You

I have not bummed across America
with only a dollar to spare, one pair
of busted Levi's and a bowie knife.
I have lived with thieves in Manchester.

I have not padded through the Taj Mahal,
barefoot, listening to the space between
each footfall picking up and putting down
its print against the marble floor. But I

skimmed flat stones across Black Moss on a day
so still I could hear each set of ripples
as they crossed. I felt each stone's inertia
spend itself against the water; then sink.

I have not toyed with a parachute chord
while perched on the lip of a light-aircraft;
but I held the wobbly head of a boy
at the day centre, and stroked his fat hands.

And I guess that the tightness in the throat
and the tiny cascading sensation
somewhere inside us are both part of that
sense of something else. That feeling, I mean.

I am – yet what I am, none cares or knows;
　　　My friends forsake me like a memory lost:
I am the self-consumer of my woes –
　　　They rise and vanish in oblivion's host
Like shadows in love-frenzied stifled throes
　　　And yet I am, and live – like vapours tost

Into the nothingness of scorn and noise,
　　　Into the living sea of waking dreams,
Where there is neither sense of life or joys,
　　　But the vast shipwreck of my life's esteems;
Even the dearest that I love best
　　　Are strange – nay, rather, stranger than the rest.

I long for scenes where man hath never trod
　　　A place where woman never smiled or wept
There to abide with my Creator, God,
　　　And sleep as I in childhood sweetly slept,
Untroubling and untroubled where I lie
　　　The grass below – above, the vaulted sky.

I Am

The Unknown Citizen

(To JS/07/M/378
This Marble Monument
Is Erected by the State)

He was found by the Bureau of Statistics to be
One against whom there was no official complaint,
And all the reports on his conduct agree
That, in the modern sense of an old-fashioned word, he was a saint,
For in everything he did he served the Greater Community.
Except for the War till the day he retired
He worked in a factory and never got fired,
But satisfied his employers, Fudge Motors Inc.
Yet he wasn't a scab or odd in his views,
For his Union reports that he paid his dues,
(Our report on his Union shows it was sound)
And our Social Psychology workers found
That he was popular with his mates and liked a drink.
The Press are convinced that he bought a paper every day
And that his reactions to advertisements were normal in every way.
Policies taken out in his name prove that he was fully insured,
And his Health-card shows he was once in hospital but left it cured.
Both Producers Research and High-Grade Living declare
He was fully sensible to the advantages of the Instalment Plan
And had everything necessary to the Modern Man,
A phonograph, a radio, a car and a frigidaire.
Our researchers into Public Opinion are content
That he held the proper opinions for the time of year;
When there was peace, he was for peace; when there was
                                        war; he went.
He was married and added five children to the population,
Which our Eugenist says was the right number for a parent of his
                                        generation,
And our teachers report that he never interfered with their education.
Was he free? Was he happy? The question is absurd:
Had anything been wrong, we should certainly have heard.

SHO NUFF

Cold soft drinks
quenched my thirst
one hot and humid July day
after a cool drive
to a mountain store.
Seems like every woman
in the place
had on halter tops
displaying their expensive tans.
There were two women
standing in front of me
at the checkout counter.
One said to the other,
'You must be a lady of leisure,
just look at your beautiful tan.'
Then the other woman responded,
'No, you must be a lady of leisure,
yours is much darker than mine.'
A tall dark and handsome Black dude
standing behind me
whispering down my Black back
s
    a
        i
            d
'Sister, if those two
are ladies of leisure,
you must surely be
a lady of royalty.'
And in a modest tone, I replied,
'SHO NUFF?'

equal
oppor
tunity

in early canada
when railways were highways

each stop brought new opportunities

there was a rule

> the chinese could only ride
> the last two cars
> of the trains

that is

until a train derailed
killing all those
in front

(the chinese erected an altar and thanked buddha)

a new rule was made

> the chinese must ride
> the front two cars
> of the trains

that is

until another accident
claimed everyone
in the back

(the chinese erected an altar and thanked buddha)

after much debate
common sense prevailed

the chinese are now allowed
to sit anywhere
on any train

99

The Choosing

We were first equal Mary and I
with same coloured ribbons in mouse-coloured hair
and with equal shyness,
we curtseyed to the lady councillor
for copies of Collins' Children's Classics.
First equal, equally proud.

Best friends too Mary and I
a common bond in being cleverest (equal)
in our small school's small class.
I remember
the competition for top desk
or to read aloud the lesson
at school service.
And my terrible fear
of her superiority at sums.

I remember the housing scheme
where we both stayed.
The same houses, different homes,
where the choices got made.

I don't know exactly why they moved,
but anyway they went.
Something about a three-apartment
and a cheaper rent.
But from the top deck of the high-school bus
I'd glimpse among the others on the corner
Mary's father, mufflered, contrasting strangely
with the elegant greyhounds by his side.
He didn't believe in high school education,
especially for girls,
or in forking out for uniforms.

Ten years later on a Saturday –
I am coming home from the library –
sitting near me on the bus,
Mary
with a husband who is tall,
curly haired, has eyes
for no one else but Mary.
Her arms are round the full-shaped vase
that is her body.
Oh, you can see where the attraction lies
in Mary's life –
not that I envy her, really.

And I am coming from the library
with my arms full of books.
I think of the prizes that were ours for the taking
and wonder when the choices got made
we don't remember making.

What-I'm-Not Song

(Finale rap)

I'm not your Little Woman
I'm not your Better Half
I'm not your nudge, your snigger
Or your belly laugh.

I'm not Jezebel
And I'm not Delilah
I'm not Mary Magdalen
Or the Virgin Mary either.

Not a Novice or a Nun.
Nor a Hooker or a Stripper.
Not Super Shirley Conran.
Not Jill the Ripper.

No I'm no Scissor-Lady –
I won't snip at your ... locks.
I'm not a siren, you're not obliged
To get off my rocks.

Not Medusa, not Medea
And, though my tongue may be salty
I'm not the Delphic sybil –
Or Sybil Fawlty

I'm not Poison Ivy
You can throw away the lotion
I'm not your Living Doll
I'm not Poetry In Motion.

And if selling Booze and Cars
Involves my body being used. Well ...
I'm not Queen Victoria
But I'm not amused.

And if you don't like my Body
You can sodding well lump it –
I'm not a Tart-with-a-Golden-Heart
Or Thinking Man's Crumpet.

I'm not your Woman of Achievement
Not your Slimmer Of The Year
I'm not Princess Diana ...
No Frog Princes 'Ere!

I'm not little Ms. Middler
I'm not little Miss Muffet
Make me An Offer I Can't Refuse –
And I'll tell you to stuff it!

'Cos I'm not your Little Woman
I'm not your Lady Wife
I'm not your Old Bag
Or the Love of Your Life

No, I'm not your Little Woman
Not your Better Half
I'm not your Nudge, your Snigger
Or your Belly-Laugh!

The Visit

We did not really want to go,
not very much,
but he said it was our Christian Duty
and anyway he had already booked the bus.
So we went
despite ourselves
dreading, half hoping to be horrified.
Through corridors with a smell,
bile greenish-yellow unfamiliar smell
of nothing we knew,
but of oldness, madness, blankness,
apathy and disinfectant.
We grinned.
We did not know what else to do.
A grimace of goodwill and Christian greetings,
hymn books clutched in sweaty palms.
We are the Church Youth Club to sing to you,
bring you the joy we have never felt.
We passed on through the strange men –
complex simple faces
so full of blankness you would not believe it –
bowing, smiling, nodding they ignored us,
or acknowledged us with sullen stares.
A tall orderly came towards us
with eyes that couldn't keep still
and a nervous twitch.
I wonder had he always been like that,
the watcher, the keeper–
calm of what prowled his cage?
We sang. The minister shut his eyes
and prayed from unironic lips
with easy phrases.

For me, only an orderly
who prayed with his eyes skinned.
Just the flick of eyes
which *can't* be everywhere at once.

In the Children's Hospital

Does it matter – losing your legs?...

SIEGFRIED SASSOON

Now let the legless boy show the great lady
How well he can manage his crutches.
It doesn't matter though the Sister objects,
'He's not used to them yet,' when such is
The will of the Princess. Come, Tommy,
Try a few desperate steps through the ward.
Then the hand of Royalty will pat your head
And life suddenly cease to be hard.
For a couple of legs are surely no miss
When the loss leads to such an honour as this!
One knows, when one sees how jealous the rest
Of the children are, it's been all for the best! –
But would the sound of your sticks on the floor
Thundered in her skull for evermore!

10

Ain't I A Woman?

(adapted to poetry by Erlene Stetson)

That man over there say
        a woman needs to be helped into carriages
and lifted over ditches
        and to have the best place everywhere.
Nobody ever helped me into carriages
        or over mud puddles
                or gives me a best place ...

And ain't I a woman?
        Look at me
Look at my arm!
        I have plowed and planted
and gathered into barns
        and no man could head me ...
And ain't I a woman?
        I could work as much
and eat as much as a man –
        when I could get to it –
and bear the lash as well
        and ain't I a woman?
I have born 13 children
        and seen most all sold into slavery
and when I cried out a mother's grief
        none but Jesus heard me ...
and ain't I a woman?
        that little man in black there say
a woman can't have as much rights as a man
        cause Christ wasn't a woman
Where did your Christ come from?
        From God and a woman!
Man had nothing to do with him!
        If the first woman God ever made
was strong enough to turn the world
        upside down, all alone
together women ought to be able to turn it
        rightside up again.

My Box

My box is made of golden oak,
my lover's gift to me.
He fitted hinges and a lock
of brass and a bright key.
He made it out of winter nights,
sanded and oiled and planed,
engraved inside the heavy lid
in brass, a golden tree.

In my box are twelve black books
where I have written down
how we have sanded, oiled and planed,
planted a garden, built a wall,
seen jays and goldcrests, rare red kites,
found the wild heartsease, drilled a well,
harvested apples and words and days
and planted a golden tree.

On an open shelf I keep my box.
Its key is in the lock.
I leave it there for you to read,
or them, when we are dead,
how everything is slowly made,
how slowly things made me,
a tree, a lover, words, a box,
books and a golden tree.

Remember?

Remember me?
I am the girl
with the dark skin
whose shoes are thin
I am the girl
with rotted teeth
I am the dark
rotten-toothed girl
with the wounded eye
and the melted ear.

I am the girl
holding their babies
cooking their meals
sweeping their yards
washing their clothes
Dark and rotting
and wounded, wounded.

I would give
to the human race
only hope.

I am the woman
with the blessed
dark skin
I am the woman
with teeth repaired
I am the woman
with the healing eye
the ear that hears.

I am the woman: Dark,
repaired, healed
Listening to you.

I would give
to the human race
only hope.

I am the woman
offering two flowers
whose roots
are twin

Justice and Hope

Let us begin.

Suggestions for exploring poetry

Poems, like people, can take some time to get to know. These suggestions include well-tested ways of working with poems that have proved to be enjoyable as well as useful.

Group readings or 'presentations'

How do you know what a poem means until you have read it? But how can you read it properly unless you know what it means? And anyway, does a poem mean the same to different people?

Explore these questions by working with others to prepare and present a reading of a poem that both reveals and reinforces its meanings. Try working in the following sequence:

i) Select a poem that might lend itself to reading aloud, like 'The Fat Black Woman's Instructions to a Suitor' by Grace Nichols, and read it for yourself.

ii) Talk together about any parts of the poem that raise questions for you.

iii) Work out how you could read it aloud, using the voices of all the group members. Avoid the boringly obvious possibilities, such as reading a verse each. Try something less predictable, such as a word each, a particular pattern of thought, or one of the 'voices' within the poem. Don't expect to be satisfied with your initial attempts, but keep trying out particular sections of the poem and see what it sounds like. Mark or underline the words you read personally and remember that it is often effective to read some parts as a chorus.

iv) Keep experimenting until you are reasonably satisfied that your reading could help listeners to appreciate the poem.

v) Find a tape recorder or an audience and present the poem.

Poetry picking

Choosing poems with a specific readership in mind is enjoyable. Working in a pair or group, decide on a focus for a collection that interests you and start selecting the poems from **Visible Voices** and other sources.

Possible collections could be:

😃 a 'Top Ten' (or Five or Twenty) of poems which you record on tape and present in an anthology for other students;

😃 a slim volume of poems intended to tempt reluctant poetry readers by offering them poems which are particularly accessible and enjoyable;

✪ a collection that might appeal to younger pupils;

✪ a selection of pre-20th-century poetry, plus a reader's guide, for students who need to meet the requirements of the National Curriculum in English;

✪ a selection based on particular poets or groups of poets;

✪ an anthology of contemporary poetry or of a particular period;

✪ poems collected on a thematic basis;

✪ collections based on particular poetic forms (e.g. sonnets or ballads).

DARTS (Directed Activites Related to Texts)

DARTS is an acronym which describes approaching texts with what has been called by Andrew Stibbs a spirit of 'intelligent irreverence'. The activities direct the reader's attention to the text more closely than usual by presenting it in unusual ways. 'Interfering' with the words and making the meaning less apparent than usual can help us to recognise that as readers we rely more on the mind's eye than on the physical eye. It can also help us to appreciate an author's techniques, as long as we finish by respecting and therefore re-reading the original text.

Guesswords or minding the gap (word deletion)

This involves finding an appropriate poem and preparing a copy of it from which some of the words have been deleted. The incomplete poem is then offered to another group, who try to suggest words which would fill the gaps.

The fun comes from deciding which words will be the best ones to delete (for example, they could be particular parts of speech, significant words, or words that only that writer would have chosen) and in eavesdropping on the conversation of those trying to think of possible words. It is also intriguing to be in the group doing the guesswork.

Remember that this is a reading activity rather than just a guessing game: what matters is that all involved should engage with a writer's intentions and achievements by recreating meanings, rather than offering 'answers' that are right or wrong.

It should be part of the process that the final stage is to re-read the whole of the text in its original form.

Poetry jigsaws or poetry pieces (sequencing)

The recipe is simple: first take a copy of a suitable poem and slice it into pieces which consist of lines or verses. Mix those pieces up and serve them to an eager pair or group of people with an appetite for poetry. Anyone who has ever done a jigsaw will understand what to do – just put the pieces in an order that seems visually and verbally appropriate, using whatever clues are available. Those clues could well include a rhyme scheme, the sound pattern of the poem or the meaning. If you are aware that the group are struggling to the point of frustration you might release such clues gradually. Remarkable though it may seem, there are times when people seem almost grateful to know about the rhyme scheme of a sonnet!

A variation on the poetry pieces theme is to take two poems with some point of similarity and to cut both up. That makes life even more interesting for those doing the twin jigsaws.

Finish by doing justice to the original by reading it in its entirety.

Poetry prediction

This is an approach for pairs, groups, or even a whole class if you have access to an overhead projector. One person, not necessarily the teacher, reveals enough of a text for the readers to gain some idea of what it is about and to begin predicting what is still to come. Keep notes on what is suggested for later reference.

A second section is revealed and people are encouraged to share their reactions and anticipations. The process is repeated until the full text has been revealed.

Discuss not just how the poet wrote the text, but how the readers interpreted it. Some poems lend themselves more than others to this approach. Occasionally there is a poem, like Valerie Bloom's 'Yuh Hear Bout?' which saves a surprise for a final line or verse in a way that can be emphasised through this degree of close reading attention.

Talking to each other

Begin by reading quietly on your own. Underline any words that puzzle or intrigue you and jot down any initial thoughts that you have. They might be questions you would like answered, words you want explained or reactions to what you have read.

Find a partner and tell each other about your initial impressions. See if you can work out between you the answers to some of your own questions. Investigate any words that need clarifying. When you reach the point where you feel unable to help each other any more, find another pair who know this poem. Take it in turns to ask each other questions that you would genuinely like to have answered.

Finish by re-reading the poem.

A Matter of Life and Death: study suggestions

Photo by Jane Brown

Tony Harrison was born in Leeds in 1937 to working-class parents and won a scholarship to Leeds Grammar School. There he 'learned Latin and learned Greek', but also learned that educated English was an 'owned language', belonging to those who regarded him as an outsider. By becoming a scholar (and an internationally renowned playwright) he earned recognition from the cultural establishment, but what he calls in one of his poems 'littererchewer' helped to cut him off from his family and his roots. He has written many poems in which the focus is on the way language is both a bridge and a barrier for a poet who feels that 'inarticulacy was part of my upbringing'. The three poems in this section reflect some of those tensions.

Book Ends

☻ Talk about the title and jot down notes on what you expected a poem with that title to be about.

☻ Tony Harrison likes rhymes because rhyme is an 'instrument of discovery... a way of monitoring, exploring, sending a radar beam into the unconscious, into the unexpected'. Underline the rhymes at the end of the lines and discuss what difference the rhymes make to you as readers.

☻ Talk about the poem's language. You might mention the quotations, the use of alliteration when so many words begin with the letter 's', and the impact of short words as opposed to long ones.

☻ Talk together about any parts of the poem that puzzle you.

☻ Take one character each and talk in role about what your character might be thinking as he sits by the grate.

☻ Discuss ways in which the father and son are alike and in which they are different.

☻ Take it in turns to read the poem aloud. Each person's task is to guide the other person on exactly how to do the reading in terms of expression and emphasis if the full impact of the poem is to be brought out.

☻ Prepare two versions of the poem, one with the sections as printed, and one with the sections in a different order, but one which still makes sense. See which version other readers prefer, and discuss their reasons with them.

🕙 What do you think the poem is about?

🕙 What do you think of the poet's ability to be so eloquent in writing about his inability to speak?

🕙 Has your view of the poem changed in any ways since you first read it? Think back over your discussions.

General assignments on Tony Harrison

🕙 Collect examples of the different 'voices' you hear through these three poems and write about the ways in which the poet brings the spoken word into his poetry. Consider these questions:

> Whose voices are they?
>
> Why did Harrison include them?
>
> What would be missing without them?
>
> What is your reaction to them?
>
> How do they contribute to the sound of each poem as well as to the meaning?
>
> Is what you know of Harrison's life and education of any significance?
>
> Which voices use dialect and what difference does this make?
>
> Does a focus on the voices in his poems help you to make any general points about Harrison's style or attitudes?

🕙 Prepare an introduction to these poems of Tony Harrison's which could help someone of your own age to understand and appreciate them. You might like to consider the following points:

> advice on which poems to read first and why;
>
> references to your own reactions when you first read the poems;
>
> Harrison's family origins, and his sense of separation from his roots;
>
> his attitude to education and to language;
>
> the images of himself and his parents that he creates;
>
> guidance as to what to look for in particular poems;
>
> explanation of words or references that might prove puzzling;
>
> his choice and use of language, given his comment that 'one of the things I've always tried to do in all my verse is to make it extremely formal, but within it to use language that is absolutely natural';
>
> why it is that Harrison is seen as one of the finest contemporary poets with a distinctive style or 'voice' that is his poetic signature.

When your introductory guide is ready in draft form, try it out on readers new to Harrison and modify it if necessary.

🕙 Conventional sonnets have 14 lines, usually divided into sections of six and eight lines. Harrison prefers a variation used by the poet

George Meredith which has 16 lines, because it allows for a balance between blocks of four and eight lines. Compare the different ways in which he uses a 16-line form in all three poems in the anthology.

⊘ Tony Harrison has said that 'the point about the form of a poem is it allows the deepest griefs to become public' and has observed, 'I think that poems are in one's own personal struggle, a momentary rescue from grief, despair, from dark thoughts'. Write about the ways in which the poet handles emotions through words by giving it 'the kind of shape that can then allow it to be shared by others'. You could comment on which emotions feature most strongly in his poems, and the direct and indirect ways in which emotion is presented and explored.

A Matter of Life and Death: general assignments

⊘ Discuss the illustrations and how they relate to the poems with which they are associated.

⊘ Compare the sonnets in this section by Christina Rossetti and John Donne. Remember that the traditional form of a sonnet is 14 lines, divided into eight-line and six-line sections.

⊘ Look in detail at Dylan Thomas's villanelle 'Do Not Go Gentle into That Good Night'. This form was French in origin and consists of 19 lines. There are five three-line stanzas (tercets) and a final four-line quatrain. The first and third lines of the opening stanza recur alternately at the end of the following stanzas, and form the last two lines of the poem. Repeating complete lines in this way is unusual – you might consider why Thomas chose to do so in a poem which was so full of passionate emotion.

⊘ Discuss with other readers why Whitman's poem was so clearly written in the 19th century and why James Fenton's could only have been written comparatively recently.

⊘ Choose two poems which explore ideas as well as feelings, and compare them in terms of language, form, tone, intention and impact.

⊘ Keep a poetry diary of your developing reactions as a reader. This demands a fairly systematic approach if it is to be effective. Note down your initial impressions of poems and compare them with your considered comments when you know the poems well and have discussed them with others.

⊘ Find examples of and write notes on the poetic function of the following aspects of language:

> *metaphors* and *similes* in 'Morning Song' and other poems;
> *onomatopoeia* in 'Out, Out –';
> the *colloquial language* in Tony Harrison's poems;
> the *archaic language* in John Donne's sonnet.

⊘ Select two or three poems in which the imagery makes an impact on you as a reader. Make notes on the images and then write a critical essay on the use of imagery in the poems.

With thanks to Carcanet Press Ltd

FEATURED POET: GILLIAN CLARKE

News Desk: study suggestions

Gillian Clarke is one of the most loved and highly regarded of contemporary poets. She was born in Cardiff and has lived in South Wales for most of her life. Hers is a distinctively personal voice and one which is rooted in the traditional music of Welsh poetry. She writes perceptively and powerfully, but unpretentiously, and when commenting on the 'music' of her poems she said, 'sometimes I use rhyme, but a poem tells me how it wants to sound. I don't decide with my head how a poem is going to sound. It must be something to do with the pace of feeling about the poem.'

It has been said of her poetry that 'her themes are large – the proximity of life and death, the interaction of the individual and family, loss and the lapse of time – but we come on them, as it were, accidentally while watching birds or visiting a neighbour or sightseeing'. She manages to encapsulate the universal in the particular, and as Anne Stevenson has written, her poetry is 'both personal and archetypal'.

Gillian Clarke often works with young writers and her poetry speaks to young readers as well as to very sophisticated ones, because she knows 'the significance of little words' and writes in a language that is both concrete and musical. She has said: 'I like to make a poem quite translucent, so that you can see a little way into it, but then I like to hide secrets inside it. They are there if you want to find them.' It is no accident that one of her poems, 'My Box', was chosen as the final poem in the television series: it speaks to us of who we are.

Sunday

❷ Prepare a copy of the poem that is without the final three lines. This would ideally be visible to a group, not just to an individual, and could be on a large sheet of paper, a computer screen or even an overhead transparency. Share the first 14 lines with people who do not know the whole poem, and invite them to guess what follows. When the time is right, offer them Gillian Clarke's ending and talk about it together.

❷ Underline the words that you notice because their sound contributes to the impact of the poem. That contribution could be through the use of proper names or:

> *assonance* – the repetition of a similar vowel sound, as in 'lunch pungent';

alliteration – the repetition of consonants in one line or in nearby lines, as in 'glistening', 'gutter' and 'glossed' or 'starved stare';

onomatopoeia – words where the meaning is echoed by the sound as in 'jump' and 'tremble';

dissonance – words that are deliberately harsh-sounding, like 'war-shriek'.

Discuss with others the words you have underlined.

General assignments on Gillian Clarke

✷ Write an introduction to the work of Gillian Clarke, based on the five poems in the anthology. Assume that your readers are preparing for GCSE and that they would be helped by information on:

> subject matter;
>
> the tone and 'music' of her poetry;
>
> imagery;
>
> vocabulary;
>
> form and structure;
>
> ideas and attitudes.

✷ Try to bring out what it is that gives Gillian Clarke such a distinctive voice as a poet.

✷ Talk together and then write about how your reactions to 'Sunday' compare with your responses to Gillian Clarke's poem 'The Field-Mouse'. Bear in mind the comments that she made in her interview for **The English Programme** that 'the death of the mouse seemed to wake up the hurt of all the terrible things that were happening in the world... a small domestic tragedy like that, a pain over the death of a little animal can set off bigger feelings, deeper feelings about the wider tragedy of people being killed in a war... the great blade of the tractor was the terrible knife of war which was cutting them down.'

✷ Comment on the claim that Gillian Clarke is not a poet of the country, but of a country, i.e. Wales. Include reference to the part played in her poems by Welsh creatures, countryside and language.

✷ Explore the ways in which Gillian Clarke links episodes from individual lives or moments of experience with wider issues and ideas. Include references to 'Neighbours' which is a poem about the international consequences of the disaster at Chernobyl, the nuclear power station in the Ukraine (*glasnost* was the term used for the opening up of Soviet society under Gorbachev that was the beginning of the end of the Communist domination of Russia and *golau glas* is the Welsh for 'blue light'). You might wish to mention Gillian's comments that 'I think one of the terrible problems today is that we are actually responsible for what is going on in the rest of the world.

In the far past, we didn't know what was happening. There were wars, there were famines, but we didn't know about them. We do know that people are starving in the world, we do know that people are being killed, but we're not doing anything about it, or at least we're certainly not doing enough. And so we feel guilty. I feel guilty. And sometimes I just can't switch the news on... I think it must have been the Sunday papers on the day I wrote 'The Field-Mouse'... we left them in a heap 'til the evening. We simply left them unread. We couldn't bear it. And somehow, not reading the newspapers gives you a few hours off from guilt, but doesn't really.'

News Desk: general assignments

⊘ Write about the use which Paul Dehn and Valerie Bloom make of non-standard English to give greater poetic effect.

⊘ Analyse and give examples of the differences between a newspaper article about Northern Ireland and the poem 'Claudy' by James Simmons.

⊘ Work with a group or a partner to prepare and record a presentation of Adrian Mitchell's poem 'Saw It In The Papers'. Keep notes on the parts of the poem that you find particularly interesting or challenging. Eventually write about how you decided on your final reading and what points you wanted to emphasise for your audience. It might be helpful to tape-record your discussions as well as your presentation.

⊘ The ballad of Sir Patrick Spens is part of our ancient oral tradition. Various versions of the ballad are available, with minor differences in detail or wording, but recognisably the same story and the same four-line quatrains. Find a different version from the one printed here by using local library resources and write a critical comparison of the two which makes it clear which one you prefer.

⊘ Use the poems by Benjamin Zephaniah and Valerie Bloom as the starting point for an essay on prejudice in print. You could refer to poetry as well as to the press.

⊘ Write about the ways in which your appreciation of Simon Rae's poem is increased by your knowledge of the original by Henry Reed.

⊘ Compare 'This Letter's to Say', written by contemporary poet Raymond Wilson, with 'The Common and the Goose' which was produced anonymously nearly two hundred years ago.

⊘ Work as a group to prepare a presentation of Desanka Maksimović's poem 'For Lies Spoken out of Kindness' and of Paul Dehn's 'Gutter Press'. Share your thoughts after working on both poems and then write up your reflections.

⊘ Try writing poems of your own, either individually or as a group, using as your starting point words from newspapers.

I Tell You I Don't Love You: study suggestions

With thanks to Virago Press Ltd

FEATURED POET: GRACE NICHOLS

Grace Nichols was born in Guyana in 1950 and came to Britain in 1977. She won the Commonwealth Poetry Prize in 1983 for her cycle of poems, *i is a long memoried woman*, and by doing so claimed a proud place for the unheard voices of the black women in her poems. Her second collection, *The Fat Black Woman's Poems*, was published in 1984 and contains the memorable anti-sizeist motto, 'It's better to die in the flesh of hope than to live in the slimness of despair'. Since then, as well as becoming a novelist and continuing to write her own poems, she has edited several collections for young people. As she has written, '...it's important for all children (black or white) to be exposed to poetry from different cultures and to be aware that black poets exist and contribute to the world's literary heritage'. She is a poet who is aware of the complexities and contradictions of categories such as 'black poet' or 'woman poet'. In the introduction to one of her collections of 'black poetry' she wrote: 'Black evokes for me, almost unconsciously, a certain cultural spirit or aesthetic with underlying connections to an African past.' The music of her poems is very varied, but it is a distinctive one that was not heard in English poetry until comparatively recently. Her subject matter is not new, since others have written about slavery, sensuality and sexuality, but her perspective on them is unique.

Even Tho

⊗ Make this poem the centre of a display that other readers might find informative and entertaining. Begin by finding visual images from magazines or newspapers which illuminate the poem. Use them to create a collage. Discuss the arrangement of the images until you are agreed as to their appropriateness and position. When you are ready, put the collage on display and invite people to look, question and read.

⊗ List the first line of each verse and then talk about the structure of the poem's developing argument.

⊗ Explore the choice and use of imagery in the poem.

⊗ Talk about the poem's language, and what you think would have been gained or lost if Grace Nichols had chosen to use standard English.

The Fat Black Woman's Instructions to a Suitor

⊗ This poem just has to be read aloud, preferably with some words or lines read by a group of voices and others by a single voice. Try a range of voice styles and accents but remember that the intention is to produce a reading that reinforces the meaning. Practise your presentation until you are really slick, and then find an audience or a tape recorder.

☻ Prepare a version of the poem which reveals all but the last line. Ask people who do not know the poem to read what they can see and to guess what might follow. Discuss the suggestions and eventually reveal the original.

☻ Try using this poem as a model for a poem of your own. Change as many words as you wish, or as few in 'The _____ _____ _____'s Instructions to a _____'.

Like a Flame

☻ Make a copy of the poem which you can cut up into sections. Give those pieces of poem to a pair or group of readers and ask them to put them in an order which satisfies them. Judge whether you need to give them additional information, such as the opening lines. When they have arrived at a version of their own, offer them the original, but not in a way that suggests that any other sequence is a failure. Finally, read the poem through in its original order.

☻ Look at the use made of 'enjambement' or run-on lines (i.e. when the unit of meaning does not necessarily coincide with the line ending). This is particularly obvious in the fifth section:

'his hands
soft his words
quick his lips
curling as in
prayer'

Talk about how this influences your reading, and see if you can find other examples in poems by Grace Nichols.

General assignments on Grace Nichols

☻ Describe and try to analyse the humour in her poems.

☻ Talk and then write about whether it is appropriate to have categories such as 'black poets', 'white poets', 'men poets' or 'women poets'.

☻ Using the evidence of these three poems, write about the ways in which Grace Nichols chooses and uses language. You might wish to pay particular attention to the impact and appropriateness of her use of non-standard English.

☻ Prepare an introduction to the poetry of Grace Nichols, based on your reading of the poems in the anthology. Assume that you are writing for people of your own age. Take as your starting point the Epilogue to her Fat Black Woman poems:

'I have crossed an ocean
I have lost my tongue
from the root of the old one
a new one has sprung.'

I Tell You I Don't Love You: general assignments

❷ Produce an illustrated version of 'La Belle Dame Sans Merci' by John Keats. Describe and explain the choices you made in terms of images in order to convey the poet's intentions and ideas.

❷ Compare the poems by Annette O'Boyle, Liz Lochhead and John Cooper Clarke, paying particular attention to their structure and language, as well as to the attitude of the poets to their 'loves'.

❷ Re-read John Donne's poem 'The Flea' and then work with a partner to produce a reader's guide to the poem. Explain any words that you find difficult to understand, on the grounds that if you find them a problem, so will other people. It is a clever poem – try to make sure that your readers appreciate how Donne builds up his central argument and remember that Donne enjoyed creating and exploring a witty idea or 'conceit'. His intentions might well have been intellectual rather than emotional.

❷ The title of Kathleen Raine's poem 'Amo Ergo Sum' (Latin for 'I love, therefore I am') is a deliberate reference to the claim by the philosopher Descartes that 'I think, therefore I am' (cogito ergo sum). Talk with other readers about how the form of the poem relates to its meaning, and discuss why the number of lines in each verse changes near the end. After your discussion write up your thoughts about the poem.

❷ W. H. Auden's 'Song' is a poem of extraordinary power, as anyone who has seen *Four Weddings and a Funeral* will know. Write a commentary on your reactions to it as a reader.

❷ Write about the contrasts between Shakespeare's sonnet 'Shall I Compare Thee to a Summer's Day?' and the poem written by Tom Leonard, so deliberately called 'A Summer's Day'. In what ways is Tom Leonard doing more than just making fun of the original?

❷ Work with a partner to prepare and present a reading of the poem 'Misunderstanding and Muzak'.

❷ E. E. Cummings made his readers work hard because he used punctuation and syntax in unconventional ways. Talk and then write about how you react to his style, and what you think of the poem 'somewhere i have never travelled,gladly beyond'.

❷ Working in a group, choose the three or four love poems you like most from this section and record them on tape with an introduction and linking commentary.

❷ Place your tongue firmly in your cheek and write a booklet of guidance for would-be love poets, giving advice on form, style, language and approach. Bear in mind that even Shakespeare found it easier to say what his love was like through comparison and personification than to describe her (or was it him?) directly.

Going Places: study suggestions

Photo by Caroline Forbes

'Whatever poetic success I've had has come from staying within the realm of my own imaginative country and my own voice.'

Heaney said this of himself in 1981. His own voice as a poet developed in spite of his consciousness of coming from generations of 'rural ancestors – not illiterate, but not literary'. He attributes his interest in words 'as bearers of history and mystery' to his mother's influence during his early years when he tuned in to the oral tradition of Ireland as well as to the voice of the radio.

He was born a Catholic in Ulster in 1939 at Mossbawn, near Castledawson in County Derry, and attended the local primary school at Anahorish. He won a scholarship to St. Columb's College in Derry and in 1957 entered Queen's University, Belfast. He was therefore shaped by the traditions of two cultures – English as well as his native Irish – but the poetic voice that is distinctively Heaney's is an Irish one.

He has a strong sense of place – many of his titles are the names of places – and as a poet he became increasingly sure of what he called 'his own ground'. The first of his poems in **Going Places** is a poem of place – 'The Plantation'. It comes from his second collection of poems called *Door into the Dark*, published in 1969. By that time Heaney was no longer a secondary school teacher, but a lecturer at Queen's University. His personal life was increasingly stable – he was married to Marie Devlin and two of their children had been born – but Northern Ireland itself was increasingly unstable because of 'The Troubles'. Heaney, as a member of the Catholic minority, was very aware of 'each element of the nightmare' – of the ways in which private lives were affected by public events and of how people and places were linked.

The earliest Heaney poem in the anthology is 'Mid-Term Break', which is about the death of his younger brother Christopher. It is in the opening section, **A Matter of Life and Death**. 'The Plantation' is one of a sequence of what Heaney himself has called 'meditative landscape poems'. They are about the sense of the past that is in the present landscape. The other two poems 'From the Frontier of Writing' and 'From the Republic of Conscience' are from his later collection *The Haw Lantern*, published in 1987.

The Plantation

Reflect on and discuss what you think of the following questions:
Who is the 'you' in the poem?
Why did Heaney begin in the centre of the wood?
Why is the first sentence longer than the first verse and why does the poet

use such short verses (or stanzas) in the first place?

What do you notice about the choice and the order of words?

What might be the significance of all the 're-passing' and the fact that someone had always been there before?

What do you make of the reference to the lovers and others?

What does the last verse mean with its references to Hansel, Gretel and the witch and to learning to lose yourself?

🔗 What do you think of the poem?

🔗 Read the poem again aloud, and give Seamus Heaney the last word.

From the Frontier of Writing

🔗 Read the poem individually two or three times and underline words that please or puzzle you. Talk about your underlined words.

🔗 Say what you thought the poem would be about when all you had read was the title.

🔗 The opening sentence lasts for the whole of the first part of the poem. Talk about why Heaney chose to have such a long sentence, and how you react to it as readers.

🔗 What do you understand by 'the frontier of writing' which is mentioned in the fifth verse ?

🔗 Is the latter part of the poem about real soldiers at all? Talk about the military imagery in the poem.

🔗 What difference does it make to have a rhyme scheme and three-line verses?

🔗 Discuss how your views of the poem have changed since you first read it.

From the Republic of Conscience

🔗 Prepare a presentation of the poem (i.e. a reading aloud with an audience in mind). Whilst you are doing so, note down any questions about the poem which you think are worth asking but which you are unable to answer. Points to consider in preparing your presentation include:

    the need to do justice to the writer's apparent intentions;

    the importance of basing your interpretation firmly on textual evidence;

    how you read the title;

    how you handle the differences between the three sections;

    how to give proper emphasis to key images;

    how your expression and your choice of voices might help listeners to appreciate what the poem is saying.

Present your reading to an audience or to a tape recorder.

General assignments on Seamus Heaney

🔗 Write about your impressions of Heaney's poetry, based on the four poems in this anthology. Points you could mention include:

    his choice of subject matter;

    the range and use of imagery;

    his choice of vocabulary;

the use made of long and short sentences in the later poems;

the use of onomatopoeia in 'The Plantation' and other poems;

how his poems are shaped and what difference the form makes;

whether your view of a poem changed with repeated reading;

which words reveal a significance that escapes you on first reading;

the impact of short words as opposed to longer ones in a poem such as 'From the Frontier of Writing';

what you have found out about the language of the poems by reading them aloud;

what you see as the typical characteristics of Heaney's poetry that give his poetry a distinctive 'voice'.

Going Places: general assignments

✆ Write about the ways Valerie Bloom and John Agard use language which is not standard English to make part of their poetic point. Consider what would have been lost if they had chosen to use only standard English.

✆ You could do worse than be a spotter of metaphors, as long as you go on to consider their contribution to a poem as opposed to just 'spotting' them. Describe and analyse the use of metaphor in poems by Simon Armitage, Keith Douglas and Craig Raine.

✆ Comment on some of the 'voices' audible in poems such as 'First Flight', 'The Metaphor Now Standing At Platform 8' and 'Not My Best Side'.

✆ Write about the ways in which various poets succeed in evoking a sense of a particular place. Suitable cases for treatment might well include Derek Walcott and Seamus Heaney.

✆ Look in detail at Shelley's 'Ozymandias' and comment on the impact made by containing such a sweep of time within the constraints of a 14-line sonnet.

✆ Choose two or three poems that have particular appeal for you and try to explain your preferences in ways that readers of your own age might appreciate.

✆ Write a reader's guide to some of the most challenging poems in this section which might help other readers to understand and appreciate the poems.

✆ If you were asked to choose from this selection just four poems, to be published for schools under the title 'Every Poem is a Journey', which poems would you pick, and why?

✆ Describe yourself as a reader of poetry, with references to the poems in this section as your evidence. You could mention:

your general attitude towards poetry;

how your approach to poetry has been influenced by your previous experience;

which particular poems or poets you prefer;

how you prefer to read poems, whether silently or aloud, alone or in a group;

how your view of some poems changed as you came to know them better;

whether you think you will read poetry later in life.

A Person is a Person: study suggestions

With thanks to Penguin Books Ltd

FEATURED POET: LIZ LOCHHEAD

Liz Lochhead was born in 1947 in Motherwell, Scotland. She trained as a painter at the Glasgow School of Art from 1965-70, but by 1972 she was already winning poetry competitions. She has been a writer-in-residence in Canada as well as in Britain, and her ability to relate to an audience during readings or workshops is legendary. She is an established playwright with a growing reputation and a distinctively Scottish voice. The ear for language that is so obvious in her plays is one of the keys to her poetry, and the poems themselves are full of characters who have voices of their own.

Many of her poems are very personal, especially the love poems, where a figure not unlike Lochhead herself (a poetic 'persona', if you prefer the technical term) is honest about the minutiae that can make us miserable. For example, in some of her poems in her *Dreaming Frankenstein* collection it is the 'you shaped depression in my pillow' or the unfamiliar brand of shampoo that triggers the pain of having parted. She is even capable of writing about the difficulty of writing about what she feels, and does so in 'A Giveaway'. That poem includes the line, 'Poets don't bare their souls, they bare their skill' and as readers we need to remember that. Lochhead helps us to do so by remarking on:

'The tripe that's talked at times, honestly –
about truth and not altering a word,
being faithful to what you felt, whatever
that is, the "First Thought's Felicity".
I have to laugh........the truth!'

I Wouldn't Thank You for a Valentine

😵 This has to be one of the best poems ever for reading aloud in a group. It was written as a rap, but it is worth experimenting with different styles and speeds. It has been argued (by the poet Jeni Couzyn amongst others) that every woman contains a range of different personalities within herself. The challenge in preparing a presentation of this poem is to identify the different facets of Liz Lochhead's persona in the poem, and to reflect those facets through various voices. There is of course nothing that says a reading requires only female voices: hearing this performed by a male voice choir could change the way an audience feels about poetry!

😵 'Swither', a word that Liz Lochhead uses in the first verse, is a 16th-century Scottish term meaning to be uncertain. This is just one example of a word that Liz has chosen because it is not the predictable standard English one. Find and talk about other examples of language choices that interest you.

❷ Show the poem to another pair or group of people, but keep the last line concealed. Ask them to write their own final lines and be rigorous about not accepting lines that do not rhyme with 'felt'. Reveal the original when you think the time is right, and discuss the various versions of the ending.

The Choosing

❷ Talk and only then write about the poet's attitude to Mary as the two girls grow older. Does she envy her really?

❷ Think about the choices in your own life that you don't remember making and yet which now seem to have been important. Re-read the poem and then write about your reactions to it as a reader. You could comment on:

the choice of words;
the impact of the long and short lines;
the point of view of the poet;
which events are mentioned and why;
what difference the use of past and present tenses makes;
how you react to Mary's father and his attitudes;
whether your thoughts are similar to the poet's, or very different.

What-I'm-Not Song

❷ This is another poem that is enjoyable to prepare as a presentation. Working as a group, try to allocate words, lines and verses to different voices in ways that reinforce the poet's meanings. It can build into a declaration on behalf of all women, rather than of just one woman.

❷ Make a list of the women referred to in the poem by name or type and try to find ways of categorising them. When you have done that, prepare a copy of the poem from which you have removed one category. Show it to other readers and see what they suggest to fill the gaps. Discuss those suggestions and finally re-read the whole poem.

❷ Liz Lochhead said that this poem was not 'a terribly angry or madly furious feminist diatribe or anything. It's just a sort of wry, tongue-in-cheek, mildly pissed off pointing out of what every woman knows already, but maybe making us laugh with recognition and enjoyment of them all being flung together with a bit of fun'. Try writing a male version of the 'What-I'm-Not Song', using the same four-line rhyming structure. When you have finished, write a commentary explaining what you were trying to do and how far you think you have succeeded.

The Visit

❷ Discuss whose eyes we are looking through as we read the poem, and what those eyes are looking at.

❷ Write a critical appreciation of the poem paying specific attention to:
choice and use of language;

subject matter;

the attitude and intention of the poet;

the form of the poem, and particularly line length;

your responses as a reader.

General assignments on Liz Lochhead

❷ Drawing your evidence from the poems in this anthology, write the introduction to a collection of Liz Lochhead's poetry which is intended for students of your own age. Refer to particular poems in detail, and where possible illustrate your points with quotations.

❷ Defend Liz Lochhead against the accusation that she is a poet who writes only for women.

A Person is a Person: general assignments

❷ Read Gareth Owen's 'A Poem For A Very Special Person' and then write your own autobiography as a reader of poetry. Begin by taking a large sheet of paper and drawing a horizontal line along the middle. Mark off that line into sections, each of which represents a year of your life. Next put in all the high points and low points of your poetry life. For example, if you remember enjoying nursery rhymes, put a dot well above the line at the appropriate time of your life. Put dots below the line if you have had a bad time, poetically speaking. When you have run out of memories, join up the dots and then write your poetry autobiography.

❷ Compare 'The Visit' by Liz Lochhead with Hugh MacDiarmid's poem 'In the Children's Hospital'.

❷ Which poem about growing up do you prefer, the one by Michael Rosen or the one by U. A. Fanthorpe? Explain your preference.

❷ Some poems, like Jenny Joseph's 'Warning', use a persona – an imagined person whose voice speaks through the poems and yet is not necessarily the poet. The word comes from the Latin term for a mask, and in some senses a persona is the poet's mask. Write about two or three poems where you think a persona has been used effectively.

❷ Describe and comment on the use of language in any two or three poems in this section. You might refer to changes in language use over time, to the impact of dialect or to the characteristics of individual poets.

❷ Look again at John Clare's poem 'I Am', which he wrote in an asylum. As you read through it silently, record your thoughts and reactions on tape and use those responses as the basis for writing a critical commentary on the poem. Pay particular attention to any aspects that you would not expect to find in a 20th-century poem.

❷ Re-read the poems in this section which you think deserve consideration for inclusion in a book for young people called 'The Poetry of Human Rights'. Working with a partner or in a group, make a short list and finally decide on which two poems you would recommend for the publication. Write about your criteria for choosing the poems and explain your recommendations.

List of Poets